W9-DCR-808

Companion Walking Tour and Audio Book

Learn more about Walking Boston—the author's private guided walking tour of Boston's Freedom Trail for families, school groups, and homeschoolers by visiting the website **WalkingBoston.com**. As a tour participant, you'll see many of the sites you experienced in the story and receive the 3 1/2 hour *One April in Boston* audio book.

Walking Boston Has 99.53% Five-Star Reviews on TripAdvisor

What tour participants are saying:

"Ben may be the closest thing you'll ever get to walking Boston with a member of the Sons of Liberty or spending the afternoon with Paul Revere himself."

"Ben truly brings history to life with a seemingly inexhaustible archive of lively stories, some of them connected in fascinating ways to the lives of his own ancestors."

"Ben has a gift for working with families and, in particular, children. As a historian, I appreciated the meticulous research and detail that went into the tour. I can't recommend this tour enough. Worth every penny."

One April in Boston

BEN L. EDWARDS

Illustrated by
CORTNEY SKINNER

Spyglass Books, LLC

One April in Boston © 2000
by Ben L. Edwards and Spyglass Books, LLC
All rights reserved

This Second Edition © 2017
by Ben L. Edwards and Spyglass Books, LLC
All rights reserved

Published by:
Spyglass Books, LLC
221 Mass Ave #1003
Boston, MA 02115 USA
ISBN 978-0-9860761-2-1

For my parents
with love and appreciation

More than 200 years ago
one young boy had a dream—
a dream he never gave up on.

He also had a very special gift
that was passed down from generation
to generation in his family.

Today, that gift is given to you.

Contents

Ben Edwards
1765-1808

Introduction

One April in Boston is the story of a real American family and a gift that was passed down from generation to generation. It was originally published in 2000. This second edition has been 15 years in the making. It was released as an eBook in 2015 and now in print form in 2017. Part 2 of the book contains details about fascinating new discoveries made during that time period and includes over 20 new illustrations created by Cortney Skinner. Most of these illustrations focus on the part of the story that takes place in the 20th century. *One April in Boston* teaches children American history, the power of imagination, and the value of goal setting.

Ben L. Edwards
Boston, Massachusetts
February 2017

In *One April in Boston* we meet 10-year-old Ben Edwards, a boy who actually lived in Colonial Boston at the time of the American Revolution. An orphan at the age of eight, he lives with his Aunt Sarah and his Uncle Alexander Edwards, a member of the Sons of Liberty. Ben is growing up at an exciting time, and his uncle's patriotic connections give special meaning to the events he experiences.

Ben dreams of a life full of adventures at sea. He wants to be a mariner, just like his grandfather, an early Boston sea captain. Ben puts this goal in writing and never gives up on it. Throughout the story, he carries a spyglass that once belonged to his seafaring ancestor. Ben believes he can glimpse the future through its lens. Some family members make fun of his claim, but not his cousin Betsey. She is certain that Ben can truly see images of things to come through his spyglass.

In *One April in Boston*, you'll meet Ben and his siblings and discover his passion for the sea. You'll encounter his Uncle Alex, a cabinetmaker, and learn about his involvement in the Sons of Liberty. You'll light the signal lanterns with Robert Newman and follow silversmith Paul Revere on his famous midnight ride to Lexington. Later, you'll stand beside Ben and his cousin Betsey as they hear the Declaration of Independence being read for the first time in Boston.

According to family legend, in 1905 the spyglass was passed on to Ben's great-great-grandson, Philip Edwards, who glimpses his own future through it. You'll follow Phil as he travels to Boston in 1909 to learn more about his ancestors. In 1917, before he goes to France to fight for his country, 22-year-old Phil kisses his sweetheart Ella goodbye and realizes that the time has come to pass on his gift.

One April in Boston is the historically accurate tale of several generations of an American family. It is the result of extensive genealogical research and is supported by online access to photographs, paintings, and artifacts, including many that have remained in the Edwards family for more than 250 years. The dialogue and many of the circumstances, events, and occurrences in the story are fictional.

Part two of the book tells readers what steps they can take to discover their own families' stories. In this section, the author shares the highlights of the search for his roots—a six-year journey that began with only a few clues.

At the conclusion of the story you'll learn what became of Ben's spyglass and where it can be found today. You'll leave with a newfound appreciation for the choices and sacrifices made by patriotic Americans from the time of the American Revolution to the present day.

So, let the journey begin ... In a changing seaport town in the colony of Massachusetts, a young boy is about to discover the roots of liberty and the birth of freedom ... *One April in Boston.*

Betsey Edwards
1765-1796

Betsey is the only other person who believes
that Ben can see the future through his spyglass.
She not only believes it, she is certain of it.

ONE APRIL
IN BOSTON

Spring at Last

April 1775

It is springtime in Boston. An active and spirited young lad races through the cobblestone streets with several of his friends. The boy has just turned 10, and memories of the long winter months, which had kept him trapped indoors, are behind him. It is a fine day to celebrate.

The boy's name is Benjamin Edwards, but nearly everyone calls him "Ben." He wears a loose fitting coat, compliments of his overprotective Aunt Sarah, and a pair of well-worn leather breeches. These two items represent the greater part of his wardrobe. In his right hand he clutches an old mariner's spyglass, a family heirloom of sorts. It once belonged to his grandfather, Captain Benjamin Edwards. Ben is seldom seen without it. He uses it to get a close-up view of daily events, but also believes that he can glimpse the future through its lens. Ben's family thinks he has a wild imagination.

Ben and his friends dash down Back Street and pause momentarily to frolic in Mill Creek. Sufficiently wet from head to toe, they stride up Middle Street where all stop to gaze up at the lofty spire of the New Brick Church. High above them, the weather vane is clearly visible against the bright blue sky. The anxious boys are halfway to their destination.

Turning down Bell Alley, the group enters North Square. Here they pass by the Old North Meeting House (Second Church). This 98-year-old wooden building was called the "Church of the Mathers." Ben's grandfather was married here in 1706 by the well-respected Puritan minister and scholar, Doctor Cotton Mather. This fact was relayed to Ben by his Uncle Alex.

As the boys reach Fish Street, they approach Paul Revere's silver shop. Ben's older sister, Sally, has an interest in Mr. Revere's oldest son, Paul Jr., but the two have yet to meet. As Ben and his friends pass the silver shop, the activity at Hancock's Wharf is finally in sight. Ben loves the sense of adventure he feels whenever he's near the water. He dreams of someday being on a sailing ship and traveling to distant shores. His frequent trips to the wharf fuel his passion for the sea.

Today, only one vessel can be seen. As the boys watch military supplies being unloaded from it, Ben uses his trusty spyglass to spot an English flag waving atop the ship's mast. His thoughts drift back to his former home on Ship Street and his father. Ben's father, Dolling, was a mastmaker at a shipyard in Boston owned by the Greenwood family. He died when Ben was only eight. Ben's mother, Rebecca Christie Edwards, had died just three years earlier. With both parents dead, the couple's four children were first left in the care of their stepmother, Hannah, and later, came to live with their aunt and uncle, Sarah and Alexander Edwards.

Ben admires his Uncle Alexander. He calls him "Uncle Alex." Alexander Edwards is a true patriot, a man with strong features and equally strong beliefs. "Town born" in 1733, the 41-year-old artisan feels a deep sense of loyalty to his fellow citizens and to Boston. A cabinetmaker by trade, Alexander learned his craft as an apprentice to Thomas Sherburne who became his guardian in 1751 after the death of his father, Captain Benjamin Edwards.

Throughout the 1750s, Alexander worked with Thomas at his shop on Back Street where they made desks and bookcases, cases of drawers, bureaus, tables of many kinds, and screens. Later, Alexander opened his own shop very close to his mentor, where he and Thomas continued their relationship, working together on many projects.

Uncle Alex and his wife, Sarah, live in a wood-frame home on Back Street. A newly constructed warehouse stands on their property, replacing one destroyed in a fire in 1773. Alexander stores materials for his business here. The rear of their land borders what remains of the "old town highway." This early route runs along the edge of the Mill Pond. A stiff breeze across Mill Cove often helps to lessen the aroma of saltwater that normally fills the air. It is a constant reminder of the town's connection to the sea.

The Edwards home is a busy place, filled with activities and laughter of the nine orphaned children in their care. The couple, having no children of their own, have made a commitment to raising not only Ben and his three siblings, but also the five children of Uncle Alex's brother, Robert, a tailor in Boston who died in 1770. Robert's five daughters lost their mother, Mary, just eight months ago.

The front door to the Edwards home opens, and Aunt Sarah appears. A kind woman, she is very capable when it comes to running a household. Ben often finds her too capable, especially when she interrupts his play to call him in for the midday meal. Shouts of "Benjamin!" fill the air. Unable to hear her now but sensing the emptiness in his stomach, Ben bids goodbye to his friends at the wharf and heads toward home.

Inside the family home, Ben's 13-year-old sister Sally helps her aunt with the cooking chores at the open hearth, while his 12-year-old cousin Rebecca assists in washing the family's clothes by hand.

"If I find that brother of yours soaked from another visit to Mill Creek," Aunt Sarah says to Sally, "he'll be scrubbing clothes and doing work for me from now until Sunday!"

A moment later, Ben bursts into the house through the front door and removes his coat. His breeches and shirt are still wet. Cousin Rebecca smiles, glancing at the pile of clothes beside her. Aunt Sarah shakes her head.

"What is to become of you, Ben?"

"I like the water, Aunt Sarah. I'm a good swimmer. Uncle Alex taught me."

"You'll be liking the water all the more when you're scrubbing your shirt in it after we eat," Aunt Sarah replies. "Now go get cleaned up." Ben dashes off toward the well in the back yard just as his Uncle Alex enters through the front door.

Ben's uncle removes the leather apron that he always wears in his cabinetmaking shop and greets Aunt Sarah with a kiss. Alexander rarely takes time in the middle of the day for a family meal, but today he has promised the children he would do so. Alexander never broke his promises, especially to his nieces and nephews, whom he loves dearly.

The Edwards family gathers around a special mahogany table for the midday meal. The table was built by Uncle Alexander as a gift for his wife. He takes great pride in everything he makes, and this fact has earned him an excellent reputation for his craftsmanship. He sits at one end of the long table, and Aunt Sarah sits at the other. Ben, Sally, their six-year-old sister Becky, and five-year-old brother Alexander are seated on one side, while their five cousins are seated on the other. These are difficult times, and the Edwards family is fortunate to have food on the table. They are thankful for it. For a brief time, all enjoy the meal without speaking a word.

Uncle Alexander finally begins the conversation.

"Thomas sends his best to everyone and especially to you, Captain." Uncle Alexander calls his nephew Ben "Captain" because of the boy's interest in the adventures of his grandfather, the mariner. Alexander adds, "Although we've been slow for some time now, we could still use some help at the shop, and you know Thomas has always pictured you as the perfect apprentice."

In the past, Ben had shown little interest in working with wood, and Uncle Alexander didn't expect much response to this, his latest effort to change his nephew's mind. Ben's thoughts are occupied daily with his love of the ocean and for sailing ships. He doesn't see how learning to build a case of drawers or repairing a table could lead to adventure on the high seas. Ben is a dreamer, and his Uncle Alex, a very practical man who feels obligated to provide his nephew with the skills required to make a proper living as a member of the artisan class. Fortunately, Alexander is also a patient man, and he feels that the proper result will occur "all in good time."

Changing the subject, Uncle Alex continues.

"I received a letter today from my brother Ben in Framingham saying that we should expect him in Boston before the week is out." Ben is Uncle Alex's older brother.

Young Ben's eyes light up.

"Uncle, he promised me that he would bring the book the next time he came to Boston. Do you think he will remember?"

"That was nearly a year ago," replies Alexander. "I haven't seen it myself since I was a boy. I wouldn't count on it, Ben."

"I hope he brings it," says Ben. "I hope, I hope."

Turning to his nieces, Uncle Alex adds, "Your aunt tells me you have all been a great help to her over the past few days. For this I am grateful."

Little Alexander, squirming in his chair and feeling left out, says, "I've been good too, Uncle Alex."

Everyone laughs.

Ben's 10-year-old cousin Betsey turns to her uncle and, in a more serious tone, says, "I don't know what we would do without you, Uncle Alex." Then she adds, "Thank you, Aunt Sarah, for taking care of us."

Providing for these nine orphaned children is the focus of Alexander's life. In doing so, he honors his brothers' memory. In the spring of 1775, Alexander has but one brother left and on Thursday, April 13, the entire family looks forward to his upcoming visit.

The Book

Uncle Alex's brother arrives from Framingham the next day, April 14, 1775. Before Ben can ask him if he remembered to bring "the book," his uncle removes a large, leather-bound volume from his saddlebags. This "book" is his grandfather's family Bible. The Bible, printed in London in 1708, was purchased by Ben's grandfather during one of his voyages at sea.

Young Ben is fascinated as he reads the many entries written in the family record section by his namesake Captain Edwards and later by other family members. The Bible is 67 years old. It lists the marriage of Captain Edwards to Hannah Harrod in 1706. It also lists the date of the Captain's second marriage in 1730 after Hannah's death, to Bathsheba Evans and the births of their seven children, including Ben's father Dolling in 1737.

As the boy turns the page, he finds a wonderful example of his grandfather's signature, penned with a flourish in the adventurous days of his youth. Fascinated, he asks Uncle Ben to tell him everything about his grandfather.

His uncle relates how an 18-year-old Benjamin Edwards "sailed for the colonies with his mother Sarah in the early

1700s after the death of his father in England. During this six-week journey, he fell in love with the ocean and decided he would become a mariner. Once in Boston, he rose through the ranks, beginning as an ordinary seaman and eventually became captain of his own vessel.

"Captain Edwards was involved in early Colonial trade with merchant ship voyages to Portugal, Mexico, Barbados, and the West Indies." Ben's eyes grow wider as his uncle continues. "He was a founder of the New Brick Church and later, a well-respected merchant in Boston. The Captain held many positions in town, including constable, scavenger, clerk of the market, and, for the last six years of his life, collector of taxes."

Overhearing the conversation, Uncle Alex enters the room carrying a framed object in his hands.

"My dear nephew, this item was packed away after it was damaged many years ago. I felt today was an appropriate time to retrieve it."

Alexander presents Ben with a painting of Captain Edwards. "This was painted in 1723," he says.

For the first time, young Ben can gaze into the eyes of someone who shared his interest in the sea. He studies his grandfather's face carefully. Uncle Ben notes that the scar on the right side of his father's chin was the result of an accident while aboard the vessel *Sarah*, a ship the Captain had named in honor of his mother.

Ben's uncle can remember tales of his father's exploits with his vessel, the *Greyhound*. "My father left Boston Harbor aboard the *Greyhound* on a cold November day in 1718. The ship contained a seasoned crew of 14 men and weighed 110 tons. Its cargo consisted of boards, staves, shingles, and fish.

The vessel was bound for a warmer climate, Antigua in the West Indies. It was protected by six guns."

"Uncle Alex, what are staves?" Ben asks.

"Staves are narrow strips of wood that are used to make barrels. A barrel maker is called a cooper. My brother John, who died in 1758, was a cooper, and he worked on a sailing ship."

Ben knew his Uncle John had been a mariner, but never realized he had been a cooper too. He says, "Uncle, if I learn to make barrels, I can go on sailing ships?"

Uncle Alex hesitates, and then replies, "If it's a way I can get you interested in working with wood, the answer is 'yes.'"

Ben smiles and thinks that working as an apprentice in his uncle's cabinetmaking shop might be a good idea after all.

As Ben continues to page through the family record section of his grandfather's Bible, he discovers a loosened page that contains the following entry: "Benjamin Edwards, son of Dolling and Rebecca, was baptized this day, April 14, 1765, at the New North Church."

"That's me!" shouts Ben.

Ben shows the entry to his uncle, who reminds him, "Today is also April 14. That line was written exactly 10 years ago."

Pointing to his first name in the entry, Ben says, "This is where they should have written 'Captain Ben.'"

Uncle Alex, understanding his nephew's meaning, responds, "If you set your mind to it, someday you'll change that line all by yourself. You can start on that journey tomorrow, my young apprentice, by helping me deliver a desk to Nathaniel Barber."

Later in the evening, before young Ben goes to bed, he decides to put his goals for the future into writing. At a tiny desk in the corner of his room, he picks up a quill pen, dips it in the inkwell, and begins his task. He drafts the following words:

> I WILL work on a sailing
> ship and see the world just
> as my grandfather did.
>
> Becoming a cooper will
> help me reach this goal.
>
> Uncle Alex can help me
> become a cooper.

"I will read this every day," he says to himself. Ben rolls up the piece of paper and tucks it away in the secret spot under his bed where he keeps his spyglass. He slips into bed and is soon asleep, dreaming of the eventful day that lies ahead.

The Apprentice

Saturday morning, April 15, is sunny and pleasant. Uncle Alex and Uncle Ben, both up since dawn, are talking in the kitchen. Uncle Ben is holding the weekly issue of the *Boston Gazette*. He begins to read part of an article out loud, and this prompts a response from his brother.

"The Colonies must stand together if we are to emancipate ourselves from that tyrant," says Alexander. "What news do you hear from the Whigs in New York and Philadelphia?"

"They view Boston as the powder keg of the revolutionary movement," says Uncle Ben. "Tensions are increasing every day. Talk in Framingham is that something will happen here, and soon."

"Then let it happen," exclaims Alexander, his fist pounding the table. "Then King George will see he cannot treat us in this tyrannical manner. His actions and policies are intolerable! We can bear their effects no longer."

Young Ben, sleeping in the next room, is awakened by his uncles' words. He had heard Uncle Alex speak passionately before about colonial rights and the economic hardship brought on by Britain's taxes on the Colonists. He remembered hearing his uncle talk about the Stamp Act—a tax on paper products, dice, and playing cards—that had been created in 1765. Uncle Alex had spoken of a protest that occurred that same year at what became Liberty Tree, a large elm tree that stands on Orange Street, close to the Common. He also described how a British tax on tea resulted in the dumping of 342 chests of it into Boston Harbor on the night of December 16, 1773. Alexander recalled a meeting he attended that same night at Boston's Old South Meeting House. After this meeting, some of the Colonists marched to Griffin's Wharf, boarded three ships, and destroyed the tea.

Perched on the edge of his bed, Ben strains to listen for more details.

"They'll surely seek out Adams, Hancock, and the other members of our party, when the time comes," Uncle Alex tells his brother. "The Sons of Liberty shall stand united against the King's soldiers and their Tory friends."

As Ben enters the kitchen, the conversation changes to a lighter subject. It is the first day of his apprenticeship as a woodworker.

His uncles greet him. "Good morning, Ben. Today, nephew, you take the first step on a long journey that will see you aboard a sailing vessel someday," says Uncle Alexander. "God willing, and with great effort, you can make it happen. Are you ready?"

"Yes, Uncle," says Ben eagerly, "but do I get to eat first?"

"If you hurry. Uncle Ben and I will head to the shop now, so be quick and don't delay. We have a busy morning ahead of us."

"Yes, sir," is young Ben's response.

After eating, Ben dashes out the front door. Less than a minute later he is back, having forgotten his spyglass. Grasping the familiar item, he is off again, running down a passageway to his uncle's shop. Charging through the door, Ben trips over a board and flies headfirst into his uncle's arms. Uncle Alex, having saved Ben from certain injury, picks up his nephew's favorite hat and sternly asks, "Does walking so disagree with you, Ben? Must you always run everywhere you go?"

"I love to run," says Ben. "When I feel the wind in my face, I imagine I'm sailing across the ocean."

His uncle shakes his head and grins.

"There will be no sailing in my shop, is that clear?"

"Yes, Uncle," replies Ben.

"Safety," adds Alexander, "is the first priority here, so we walk. However, that should not discourage your sailing, or running around Boston outside of the shop."

Ben smiles.

The cabinetmaking shop contains three items in different stages of production. In the far corner is a bookcase Ben's uncle is repairing for Moses Gill. Next to it is a case of drawers he is building for Grant Webster. Both men are regular customers. In the center of the floor stands the only finished item in the shop. It is a desk, constructed of mahogany. At first glance, it looks like a case of five drawers with a slanted top. The top has a fanciful design that resembles some sort of star, or maybe a serpent. Young Ben watches as his uncle slides out two wooden rails from the front of the cabinet, then unlocks the top. As the hinged top is lowered, it comes to rest on the wooden rails. The transformation reveals a wonderful desk, complete with several drawers and secret compartments.

Uncle Ben recognizes the design immediately. It matches their grandfather's desk, brought to the Colonies from

England some 70 years ago. Uncle Ben keeps the original desk at his Framingham home. He had sent his brother drawings of it nearly six months ago with little confidence that Alexander would be able to duplicate it. To his surprise, it looks exactly like the original.

"Alexander," he says, "you have become a true craftsman. Your talents surprise even me." Alexander is pleased with his brother's words.

The desk is placed on Alexander's wagon. He retrieves his trusted horse from the barn and hitches him to the wagon. All three climb aboard.

"Where does Mr. Barber live?" asks young Ben.

"Nathaniel lives on Charter Street," responds his uncle. The wagon travels along Back Street to its intersection with Prince Street. Salem Street is just ahead. As the wagon travels up Salem Street, young Ben notices the confident stride of three British Regulars. He and his friends call them lobster-backs, because of the bright red coats they wear. Their occupation of the town is a constant source of anger for Ben's uncles, who now ignore the soldiers' presence.

On the right, just three blocks from the Edwards home, Christ Church appears. The brick building is topped by a three-tier, 191 foot steeple. Ben's uncle stops the wagon a short distance beyond the church in front of Nathaniel Barber's home, located near the intersection of Salem and Charter streets. A large man stands outside the front entrance to the modest wooden dwelling. He greets Uncle Alex with a warm handshake. The two men are longtime friends.

"It's perfect," bellows Nathaniel, as he inspects the desk.

The three men take the desk off the wagon and carry it through the front door of the Barber home. They then sit down for a drink and begin to talk. Young Ben asks his uncles if he can wait outside so he can look at the steeple of Christ Church. Alexander responds, "Yes, but stay close by, as we will be leaving soon."

Ben steps outside into the crisp Boston air. The sun shines brightly. Just then, the breeze picks up, and he clutches his hat moments before the wind would have taken it. Ben peers at the steeple of Christ Church through his spyglass. Through the lens, he sees a single flicker of light and then a second in the top window of the steeple. "What could that be?" he wonders out loud.

Ben imagines what the view would be like from that same window. Soon, he has "that look" on his face, the one his Aunt Sarah always notices when he's about to get himself into "some real trouble." Sensing he has the time, Ben runs down Salem Street toward the church, hoping that he might somehow get in. To his surprise, he finds the door slightly open, and he slips inside.

Young Ben walks down the aisle of the church, passing the high box pews on either side. As he gets closer to the pulpit, a voice rings out in a rather strong tone.

"Can I help you son?"

Ben turns, staring into the eyes of a large man. It is Captain John Pulling Jr. John is a member of Christ Church and the Sons of Liberty.

"What's your name, lad?" he asks.

"Ben Edwards, sir," responds Ben, rather sheepishly.

"Edwards ... of any relation to Alexander Edwards?"

"He is my uncle, sir. He is up the street delivering a desk to Mr. Barber."

"I know your uncle. He is a fine man. My name is John," he says extending his hand, "John Pulling." Just then another man appears.

"It's all right, Robert," says John. "I know this lad's uncle. He means no trouble." Robert Newman, the church sexton, appears concerned by the intrusion. Sensing that time is running short, Ben gathers his nerve and asks John a question.

"The steeple, sir, is it really the tallest in Boston—even taller than the New Brick?"

"That it is, son," is the reply.

Taking a deep breath, Ben continues.

"Can you see Charlestown from it, sir, and any ships on the Charles River on a clear day ... like today?"

John Pulling grins, admiring the lad's persistence, then glances at Robert Newman. The sexton shakes his head, but after more convincing, reluctantly agrees to the request.

"Follow me, lad, and you can see for yourself," is John's response.

Ben follows his newfound friend up a flight of wooden steps that leads to a landing. From here, they go through a door, up more steps, and reach a second landing. From this location, the bells are rung for church services. They continue up additional steps and finally climb a series of ladders that lead past the bells to a trap door and the top of the steeple.

Ben had never seen the town from such a vantage point before. Through his spyglass, he can see beyond Hudson's Point to Charlestown. There is no guarantee he will see a sailing ship. The Boston Port Bill of 1774 had closed Boston Harbor to all but the King's warships. It would not be reopened until the Colonists paid for the tea they had destroyed in 1773.

Soon, Ben grows excited as a large military vessel comes into view. Its magnificent sails are caught in the stiff breeze. It is just what he had hoped to see. John points out Copp's Hill and several of the shipyards.

"That's a fine spyglass you have there," comments John.

"It belonged to my grandfather," says Ben. "He was a sea captain who traveled across the ocean. That's what I want to do ... someday."

"And do it you shall," says John. "Never stop believing in your dreams, lad, for it is that belief—combined with hard work—that guarantees everything you imagine will someday come true. Your Uncle Alexander and I share the same dreams. We dream of liberty for the Colonies, freedom from England, and the right to govern ourselves. However, even our dreams will remain 'just dreams' unless we are committed enough to act. You too lad must commit yourself. Take some action each day that will bring you closer to the course you have chosen. Remember these words, lad, and never forget this view I have given you today."

"Thank you, Mr. Pulling," replies Ben. "I'll never forget this day! Before we leave I must tell you that I saw two flickers of light in this window before I entered the church."

"Flickers of light?" responds John. "Likely a reflection in the windowpane."

"Perhaps," agrees Ben, "but the window was open, sir. Maybe it's a reflection of things to come."

"Quite an imagination you have there, lad, and where might that come from?" asks John.

"I see things through my spyglass, but only my cousin Betsey believes me. Do you believe me, Mr. Pulling?"

"Don't mind what others say, Ben. Believe in yourself. That's all that matters."

As Ben considers the response, John turns around and opens the trap door that leads to the ladder below.

"Be careful now, Ben," says John. "Both my friend Robert and your Uncle Alexander will want you back in one piece." Ben slowly and carefully follows his guide down the ladders, past the bells, and finally down the narrow steps that lead to the floor of the church.

Lost in the moment, young Ben barely hears his uncles' call as they search for him.

John leads Ben outside through the front door, and they spot his two uncles approaching.

"Well, good day to you, John. I see you've met my nephew," exclaims Alexander. "I was beginning to think he'd run off to the wharf. I hope he caused you no trouble."

"No trouble at all," says John. "He's a fine lad with a sharp mind and a love for the sea, I'd say. I gave him a view of our town that few children have seen—a view from the top of the highest steeple in all of Boston."

Young Ben had such a grin on his face that Uncle Alex didn't have the heart to scold him.

"John, this is my brother, Ben. He is visiting us from Framingham. He is active in the militia and in the service to our cause for liberty. Ben, this is my friend Captain John Pulling Jr."

Uncle Ben and John shake hands.

"Alexander, your nephew tells me you were delivering a desk to Nathaniel Barber. Would that be the desk you felt would be such a challenge?"

"That it would be, John. It was indeed a challenge, but I am rather pleased with the outcome. You may call on Nathaniel and view it yourself. I would value your opinion, John. Can I interest you in a case of drawers or a chamber table this spring?"

"Sadly, times are difficult thanks to the Coercive Acts of King George. For now, we will have to make due with the furniture we have."

"Thank you for looking after my nephew, John. We will speak again soon."

Young Ben adds, "Thank you, Mr. Pulling, for everything you've shown me."

John pats Ben on the head and says, "You're most welcome, lad. Now it's back to the day's business." At that, John Pulling steps back into the church and seeks out his friend Robert Newman.

Uncle Alex finally addresses young Ben.

"Now I see why you try your aunt's patience at times, Ben. Although she tries, she cannot understand you ... but I can. You remind me of myself when I was your age, full of energy, ideas, and always into mischief. Ah, to be 10 years old again."

"Uncle, Uncle," Ben exclaims, "I could see clear across to Charlestown. I saw a sailing ship on the Charles and many of the shipyards, too. It felt like I was on top of the world!"

The experience has somehow changed Ben. He pledges that his desire to learn the woodworking trade from his uncle is sincere.

"Starting Monday I will be at the cabinetmaking shop bright and early to help you. I can clean up, and I promise I will walk and not sail when I sweep the floors. Please teach me, Uncle Alex. I will make you proud."

The two uncles exchange winks, and all three climb aboard the wagon and begin the short trip to their next stop.

Uncle Alexander

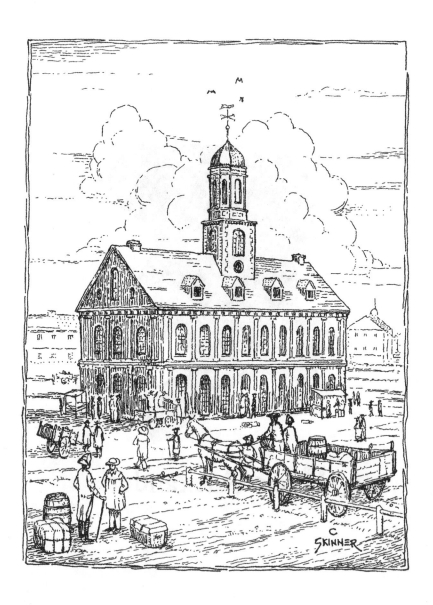

The Sons of Liberty

Ben and his uncles travel up the hill directly across from Christ Church. This is Hull Street. To their right lies Copp's Hill Burying Ground. Ben had seen Copp's Hill from the steeple of Christ Church. Uncle Alex wishes to visit the family tomb located here.

Tomb Number 5 has its entrance near Hull Street. A simple slate marker above it reads "Capt. Benjamin Edwards Tomb." It was constructed by Ben's grandfather in 1717. It is the final resting place for the sea captain and his many relations, including Uncle Alex's brothers John, Robert, and Dolling (young Ben's father). Ben's uncle stops by often to pay his respects.

Young Ben stands beside his grandfather's slate marker and thinks longingly of his parents. He reaches into his pocket and pulls out a small scrap of wood from his uncle's cabinetmaking shop. He places this piece of wood on top of the marker. Wishing to show evidence of his visit, Ben performs this ritual each time he comes here. Before they leave, Uncle Alex decides to look for the marker of a friend he had known six years earlier. After a careful search, he spots the stone.

The man had died at the age of 44, just two months after Uncle Alex had last seen him at Robinson's Tavern in

Dorchester. Both men dined there on August 14, 1769, with over 300 other members of the Sons of Liberty. Before the dinner, the group had gathered at Boston's Liberty Tree. Uncle Alex kneels down next to the stone and, holding his nephew's hand, he begins to read the inscription aloud:

"Here lies buried in a Stone Grave 10 feet deep, Capt. Daniel Malcom Mercht, who departed this Life October 23d 1769, Aged 44 Years, a true son of Liberty, a Friend to the Publick, an Enemy to oppression, and one of the foremost in opposing the Revenue Acts on America."

There was that phrase again, "a Son of Liberty." Ben had heard his uncles mention it earlier that morning as he listened from his room. It sounded like a big secret. Ben decides to find out what it is. He will ask his Uncle Alex before the day is out. As the men leave Copp's Hill, they head toward their third stop of the day. They will travel in the opposite direction, due south, to the merchant exchange on the ground floor of the Town House. Uncle Ben has some business to conduct there. It is one of his reasons for coming to Boston.

The group passes by the Edwards home on Back Street and travels over the bridge at Mill Creek. The fastest route takes them down Hanover and Brattle streets to Queen Street. This route avoids the busy area by the Town Dock. Queen Street is the back entrance to the Town House, which is located at the head of King Street, near Long Wharf.

On Queen Street, the wagon approaches the printing shop of Benjamin Edes and John Gill. As members of the Sons of Liberty, the printers offer complete support to the patriot cause. Their shop contains a hand-operated printing press, a few fonts of type, and a small office. Edes and Gill are inside, setting type for Monday's issue of the *Boston Gazette*. As the wagon reaches the shop, Uncle Alex notices two men exiting from the office door. Both of them are prominent Boston Whigs. As the wagon passes, he bids "good day" to John Adams and James Otis.

As they reach King Street, Uncle Alex stops the wagon and Uncle Ben goes inside the Town House for a brief meeting. Young Ben looks up at the impressive brick building. On the second story, a balcony extends out. The royal governors make their official proclamations to the Colony from this location. Farther up near the gable, on either side, Ben can see statues of a lion and a unicorn. These royal symbols are a constant reminder of British rule and the Colonists despise them. Uncle Alex mentions that the Boston Massacre, which Ben had heard him speak of before, took place in front of this very building on the night of March 5, 1770. British soldiers killed five men here, including his friend Samuel Gray.

After Uncle Ben finishes his business at the merchant exchange, the three travel a short distance to Merchants Row by Faneuil Hall. Alexander has promised Aunt Sarah he would pick up some items at a shop located here. Faneuil Hall is Boston's town meeting hall. It was the first place where Colonists dared to speak out against the rule of the mother country. Merchants Row is a marketplace for goods and services.

Uncle Alex seeks some fabric that Aunt Sarah needs to make clothes for the children. Once the fabric is located and purchased, the day's busy schedule is complete. Before leaving, Alexander brings his nephew's attention to the weather vane at the top of the meeting hall. Every true Bostonian knows its story. It is a grasshopper, fashioned by master craftsman Shem

Drowne. Constructed of copper and gold leaf, with glass doorknobs for eyes, it measures 52 inches long and weighs 38 pounds. The symbol was chosen by the building's benefactor, Peter Faneuil, and placed atop the hall in 1742. Some townspeople say it was modeled after a similar weather vane that sits on the roof of the Royal Exchange in London. To Ben, it is so high in the air that it looks as small as a real grasshopper. But, trusting his uncle's story, he becomes convinced that it is indeed "Boston's biggest bug."

The afternoon is getting late, and Ben and his uncles start the journey home. Ben is very hungry. Normally fussy about what he eats, at this moment he would devour anything his Aunt Sarah placed in front of him. As the wagon nears Mill Creek and draws closer to the Edwards' home, he decides to ask the question.

"Uncle Alex ... who are the Sons of Liberty?"

Alexander, wondering how to respond, looks to his brother Ben.

Uncle Ben considers the question carefully and then begins to speak: "Liberty is the God given right of all men. The Sons of Liberty were formed to protect that right and fight against all those who would seek to limit it. King George wishes to impose his will and taxation policies on us while giving us no voice in the matter. His Regulars have invaded our town and our lives. With the aid of the Sons of Liberty, and for the future of our children, this will not stand. Freedom is on our doorstep, Ben, but it won't come without a struggle. I feel, my dear nephew, that you will soon witness the birth of that freedom."

Uncle Alex, appreciating his brother's comments, nods his head in agreement.

As young Ben hops off the wagon, he isn't quite sure what his uncle's response meant. He is, however, more convinced than ever that his uncles are somehow involved in this cause for liberty, and that makes him feel proud.

Before entering the house, Ben asks, "Can I be a Son of Liberty, Uncle Alex?"

Uncle Alex laughs and then whispers, "Only if you agree to speak of it to no one but me and if you help your aunt more with her work."

Young Ben thinks for a moment, then replies, "I will, Uncle. Now let's eat, so I'll have some dishes to clean!"

Ben and his two uncles agree that food has never tasted so good. With all the family together, Ben tells the other children how he climbed to the top of the steeple at Christ Church. Never willing to believe his tall tales, his cousin Rebecca replies, "Was it before or after you carried the desk in by yourself, Ben?"

Ben's cousin Betsey is not as skeptical.

"You must have seen all of Boston from there and even Charlestown!"

"I did, Betsey! I saw a large sailing ship on the Charles, too, just like the one I'll be on someday."

Sally and Rebecca giggle at that idea. Ben ignores their laughter and continues.

"I wish you had been with me, Betsey."

"So do I," she adds. "Will you take me next time, Ben?"

Although Ben realizes he may never get another chance to climb to the top of the steeple, he tells his cousin, "Next time, Betsey, we'll go together. I promise."

After a lengthy explanation, Uncle Alex convinces the other children that Ben's story is true. Remembering the deal he has made, Ben begins to clean the dishes for his aunt without being asked. His behavior surprises everyone except his uncles.

Before the family leaves the table, Cousin Rebecca asks, "What time will we be leaving for church in the morning?"

"The usual time," says Aunt Sarah.

Rebecca turns to her cousin Sally and says, "We're sure to see Paul at tomorrow's service. Would you please speak to him before the other girls catch his eye?"

Aunt Sarah says, "Rebecca, you're not stirring up trouble now, are you?"

Rebecca grins, points to herself, and innocently asks, "Me, Aunt Sarah?"

Uncle Alex shakes his head.

A few hours later, after Aunt Sarah has tucked all the children into bed, young Ben reaches under his bed to retrieve the piece of paper he had hidden near his spyglass. With the help of the moonlight illuminating his room, he reads the words he had written yesterday. "I WILL work on a sailing ship and see the world just as my grandfather did. Becoming a cooper will help me reach this goal. Uncle Alex can help me become a cooper." He repeats this over and over again as he pictures the great sailing ship he spotted from the steeple earlier in the day. As he falls asleep, he is aboard that vessel, traveling with great speed toward some unknown coast. On this night, Ben the cooper is living a life full of adventure. In his dreams, his grandfather and a tall friend sail along with him.

As Ben sleeps, Alexander readies himself for his responsibilities this night. With a wink and a loving look, he bids Aunt

Sarah goodnight and slips out the back door. He walks several blocks from his home to the Green Dragon Tavern. Here he meets with other members of the Sons of Liberty. They discuss the latest news about the movements of the British troops. He returns home several hours later, just as the clock strikes midnight, marking the coming of the Sabbath day.

Rebecca Edwards

A Day of Rest

The Sabbath is a day for rest and reflection—a day to give thanks to God for his good graces. The Edwards attend services at the New Brick Church faithfully. Everyone rises early on the morning of April 16, 1775. The children dress themselves in their best clothes, with the girls wearing petticoats, short gowns (jackets), and mob caps fashioned by their aunt.

Sally's auburn hair beautifully accents the rose-colored fabric of her homespun short gown. She presents an appearance that all find most endearing and attractive. Always focused on doing what is best for the family, Sally is a hard worker with a positive outlook on the future. Occasionally shy—especially around a certain boy she fancies—Ben's sister dreams of someday having a family of her own.

Her cousin Rebecca is outgoing and mischievous. She is less concerned about appearance and more focused on having fun. It is a character trait that she certainly shares with her cousin Ben. Like Sally, she is a diligent worker, but also has a reputation for getting into mischief. Her most distinctive feature is her big brown eyes. Aunt Sarah often notes that Rebecca looks very much like her late mother, Mary Edwards.

Today, young Ben wears the same baggy knee breeches he always wears, and a loose shirt. Over that shirt, he wears a green waistcoat (vest) fashioned with tie-on sleeves. Uncle Alex, his brother Ben, Aunt Sarah, and the children gather in front of the Edwards home to begin the short walk across Back Street and down Beer Lane to Middle Street, where the church is located. A chill is in the air on this overcast spring morning.

The New Brick Church is a prominent landmark in Boston. The church is regarded as a building of uncommon elegance and taste. Its unique steeple is topped by a weather vane shaped like a rooster, giving locals reason to call it the "Cockerel Church."

The weather vane was hammered out of brass kettles many years ago by Deacon Shem Drowne. The building has entrances on the west, south, and east. Responding to a slight breeze, the weather vane points due north as members of the parish fill the church for the early morning service.

The Edwards family enters the New Brick Church from the west side, and Uncle Alex leads them down the broad aisle to the family's square pew, noted as Number 28 in the church records. This pew, originally purchased by Ben's grandfather, has been held by members of the Edwards family for more than 50 years. Young Ben fidgets in his seat as more parishioners fill the church. He glances at the upper level where a few of the younger children are playing.

Rebecca nudges her cousin Sally, and they both turn around noting the entrance of Rachel Revere, wife of silversmith Paul Revere, and two of her children, Deborah and Paul Jr. The Revere family sits in pew Number 59.

"You must speak to him," Rebecca tells Sally, "he looks at you when we leave after every service."

"I was hoping he'd approach me," responds Sally quietly.

Rebecca shakes her head realizing that at this rate, 15-year-old Paul Revere Jr. and her cousin would never become acquainted. Scheming as always, Rebecca has a plan of her own to speed the process along.

Reverend Ebenezer Pemberton, the 70-year-old pastor of the New Brick Church slowly makes his way to the pulpit that stands in the middle of the building's north side. After a brief pause, waiting for all to become attentive, he begins preaching the sermon. The service itself lasts just under an hour. Toward the end, Reverend Pemberton shares some of his own personal views about England, her colonies, and the current tensions. Opinions of the congregation appear split on his view of this topic.

When the service ends, Uncle Alex leads the family out of the church, and he stops for a moment to speak with friends. Rebecca takes this opportunity to set her plan into motion. Before Sally can prevent it, Rebecca engages in a conversation with Paul Revere Jr. Her message soon brings a smile to his face, and then they both share in some hearty laughter.

By this time, Sally has noticed the two speaking and wonders what her cousin is up to. A moment later, Rebecca brings Paul over to meet Sally.

"Your cousin says that you intend to marry me someday and predicts we'll have a large family ... at least 10 children, according to her!" says Paul. "Perhaps we should begin by saying hello. My name is Paul Revere Jr."

"My name is Sally Edwards."

"Well, Sally, your cousin suggests we name our first son after your Uncle Alex."

Sally, appearing quite embarrassed, glares at her cousin Rebecca, who is now grinning from ear to ear.

"I have to leave soon with my family," says Paul. "It was very nice meeting you, Sally," and, winking at Rebecca, he adds, "thanks to you."

Paul Jr. dashes off to join his mother and his sister Deborah. The church land connects directly to their North Square property, and for the Reveres, it is a short walk home.

Outside of the church, the conversation continues.

"I think he really likes you," says Rebecca.

Sally, about ready to explode, says, "At least 10 children! I hope you prayed well this morning because you'll need some of those prayers to save you now."

With that, Sally lunges for her cousin and then chases her for the full distance back to the Edwards home. Fortunately for Rebecca, she never quite catches her.

Back at the church, the fun and frolic of a budding romance is replaced with the reality and serious nature of what lies ahead. Uncle Alex has just concluded a conversation with several men. There is real concern that the British Regulars are preparing for some sort of movement, perhaps an expedition into the surrounding countryside, in the very near future.

Absent from the services this morning and from his usual seat in pew Number 59 is silversmith Paul Revere. He awoke before daybreak at his home in North Square and is off on an errand for the Sons of Liberty. Before this day is out, he will travel to Lexington, Concord, and back through Charlestown. In Lexington, at the Clarke house, he will meet with

John Hancock and Samuel Adams and then warn the militia at Concord to scatter and conceal their store of weapons and gunpowder. On his return trip through Charlestown, later this evening, Revere will meet with a patriot named Colonel William Conant. Paul Revere will tell Colonel Conant of his idea for a signal to notify the Sons of Liberty in Charlestown of the time and route of the Regulars' march.

As the Edwards family walks toward Back Street on their way home from church, Ben notices that something has changed. There is a look of concern on both his uncles' faces. He recalls a recent conversation, and how his Uncle Ben spoke of the birth of freedom and a struggle that would come. As the family walks on in silence, for a reason he can't quite explain, Ben senses that the time for this struggle is drawing near.

Two Lanterns

On Monday morning, April 17, the Edwards family gathers to bid goodbye to their special guest from Framingham. The family Bible and Uncle Ben's other documents are safely packed for the return trip. After a warm handshake from his brother and hugs from Aunt Sarah and the children, Uncle Ben rides off on horseback, out Boston Neck, and toward his Framingham farm.

After bidding his uncle goodbye, young Ben follows his Uncle Alex to the cabinetmaking shop. When they arrive, they're greeted inside by Thomas Sherburne. Mr. Sherburne is a short, stocky man with a quick wit and an engaging personality.

"Welcome aboard, Captain," he bellows.

"Good morning, Mr. Sherburne," responds Ben. "I am here to learn the woodworking trade."

"Ah, you've decided to become a cabinetmaker after all."

"Actually, I'd like to learn to make barrels. Can you teach me?"

"You want to be a cooper?" says Mr. Sherburne with surprise, as he glances over the top of his spectacles. "Why make barrels when you can create fine furniture like this?" he adds, pointing to the intricate case of drawers he is working on.

"Uncle Alex told me that coopers can work on sailing ships," responds Ben, "and that is what I'd like to do."

Mr. Sherburne explains that he doesn't have all the tools that a cooper would use, but he could get them in the future if Ben was really interested. Thomas is a very skillful man who has knowledge in many areas. He offers Ben training in the basic skills he will need to become a successful cooper in exchange for his help at the shop. Ben happily agrees to the arrangement by saying, "Thank you, sir." Smiling at his Uncle Alex, he adds, "I am ready to start as your apprentice, Uncle!"

On the 17th and 18th of April, Ben works at the cabinet-making shop. He cleans up, sweeps the floor, and learns about the tools used in the cabinetmaking trade. Uncle Alex and Mr. Sherburne use saws, drawknives, planes, and other specialty tools to shape their work. He will use similar tools one day as a cooper.

Ben is amazed as he watches ordinary pieces of wood being transformed into a case of drawers. He sees his uncle repair a badly damaged bookcase. His appreciation for the talents of Mr. Sherburne and his Uncle Alex grows by the hour.

On the evening of April 18, Ben is in bed by 8 p.m. Though tired after two full days of work, he tosses and turns, finding it difficult to fall asleep. Soon it is 9 p.m., and most of the other members of the family have gone to bed as well. Ben stares at the wooden beams in the ceiling of his small room. Light from the night sky peeks through his window and casts shadows on the wall. In Ben's imagination, these shadows become the King's soldiers, dressed in uniform and carrying muskets. "Why can't I fall asleep!" he mumbles to himself. "I have to be up early for work." Finally, out of pure frustration, he decides to get up.

Thos. Sherburne

Ben fumbles in the darkness for the spyglass he keeps beneath his bed. After finding it, he puts on his breeches and, in his nightshirt, walks barefoot through the kitchen and steps outside through the back door. He stares at the stars through his spyglass and watches them hide behind a wisp of clouds and then reappear. This game of hide-and-seek goes on for several minutes as the stars glimmer brightly over the town. Then Ben notices something odd. As he watches, the stars move into a circular shape. Ben counts them ... 1, 2, 3, ... a total of 13 stars form a circle in the night sky above Boston.

When he takes the spyglass away, the circle vanishes. Ben rubs his eyes, yawns, and peeks through his spyglass once again. The circle of 13 stars returns. Ben has always believed he can see the future through the lens of his grandfather's spyglass, but this message—these 13 stars united as one—what was it telling him? Confused and finally feeling tired, Ben walks back inside, lies down on his bed, and, once again, tries to fall asleep. The time is 9:30 p.m.

Across town, a message has been delivered to Paul Revere. The Regulars have begun to gather for their march, and Revere is wanted immediately at the home of patriot leader, Dr. Joseph Warren. This is the moment that Paul Revere has prepared for. In a matter of minutes, he arrives at his good friend's home where an anxious Warren asks him to leave immediately for Lexington. He must notify Samuel Adams and John Hancock that the soldiers are moving. There is a good chance that Adams and Hancock are in danger. Revere learns that Warren has already sent another messenger rider, William Dawes. Revere knows Dawes, who is one of his neighbors.

Dawes's route will be hazardous because he will have to ride out through the British guards on Boston Neck. Revere's route, across the Charles River by rowboat to Charlestown, will be equally dangerous. The chances of both messengers getting through to Lexington is far from certain. Revere realizes this. During his recent visit to Charlestown, he told members of the Sons of Liberty about his idea for a signal that will alert them to the movement and route of the British troops. The signal will insure that this vital information is delivered to Adams and Hancock even if both messenger riders are captured or delayed. This pre-arranged signal involves showing lanterns briefly in the steeple window of Christ Church in Boston: "one lantern" if the troops would march "by land" out Boston Neck and "two lanterns" if they would row "by water" across the Charles River to Cambridge. After talking to Dr. Warren, Revere knows that the signal will be "two lanterns."

At about 10 p.m., Paul Revere leaves in great haste from Dr. Warren's home and cautiously makes his way to the corner of Salem and Sheafe streets and the house of Robert Newman, the sexton of Christ Church. Looking through a window into the Newman home, Revere is concerned to see a party of British army officers laughing and playing cards at a parlor table. The Newman family is renting rooms to these British officers in order to make ends meet during hard times. It seems unlikely that Robert Newman would be able to exit the home without being spotted by them. For a moment, Revere hesitates, and his thoughts race. What if he cannot contact Newman? The sexton has the only key to the church. Without him there will be no signal to the Sons of Liberty in Charlestown. Paul Revere considers what to do next.

Fortunately, 23-year-old Robert Newman had the sense to foresee Revere's situation. Just before Paul Revere's arrival, he bid the officers goodnight and pretended to go to bed early. Instead, he opened a window in his chamber, climbed outside, and dropped to the garden below. Newman gathered here with another Revere associate, Captain John Pulling Jr., and a neighbor, Thomas Barnard. The three men awaited Revere's arrival. Now, as Paul Revere stands in the darkness outside the sexton's home, Newman, Pulling, and Barnard greet him. He gives the men their instructions, and the plan is set into motion.

It is 10:15 p.m. as Paul Revere's three associates make their way to Christ Church. Revere returns to his home in North Square, which is just several blocks away. He quickly gives his wife Rachel the news and she helps him as he gathers up his riding boots and long surtout. Rachel kisses her husband and expresses concern for his safety. A moment later, as 15-year-old Paul Revere Jr. peeks from his bedroom window, his father races off into the darkness.

Revere heads toward the waterfront, where a boat had been hidden for him beneath the wharf. On the way, he seeks out two friends, Joshua Bentley and Thomas Richardson, both experienced boatmen. They will row Revere across the Charles River.

Meanwhile, back at Christ Church, Sexton Robert Newman and Captain John Pulling Jr., now inside, gather two square metal lanterns from the entry hall closet, where Newman had hidden them. The sexton places flint, steel, and a tinderbox to light the lanterns in his pocket. Outside the church, Thomas Barnard stands guard. Newman and Pulling, each carrying a lantern, begin the long climb up into the church steeple. At the second landing, a ray of light shining through the round window in front of the church illuminates their path, if only for a moment. The climb continues up more stairs, to a series of ladders that Robert Newman and Captain John Pulling Jr. must navigate in pitch darkness. They climb past the bells and reach the high glass windows in the steeple of the church. Here, Robert Newman prepares the lanterns for lighting. The time is just past 10:30 p.m.

With flint and steel in hand, Robert Newman creates a spark and then fans a small flame in his tinderbox. First he lights the candle in one lantern, and then, the candle in the second. Finally, with a look of determination, Captain John Pulling Jr. pushes up the wooden window frame and the men hold two lanterns aloft in the northwest window of Christ Church, facing Charlestown. The flames flicker, and then burn brightly. The signal has been sent.

CORTNEY
SKINNER

Only Newman and Pulling can determine how long to display the lanterns. Once they sense the time is right, the men blow out the candles, close the window, and carefully make their way back down to the floor of the church. Hearing noises in the street and fearing they may be coming from a British patrol, Newman and Pulling decide it is not safe to leave through the front door. They return the lanterns to the closet and, bending below the level of the high box pews, make their way down a side aisle and enter the last pew near the altar. Here, they raise the window in front of them and climb out, lowering themselves to the ground. The men part ways quickly. Captain John Pulling Jr. heads in the direction of his mother's home while Robert Newman cautiously walks to his own home where he climbs through a rear window to join his wife Rebecca in their bed. In a matter of moments, the exhausted sexton is asleep.

A few blocks away, at the Edwards home on Back Street, 10-year-old Ben Edwards is also fast asleep. When he awakes in about eight hours, the Boston he has known so well will be forever altered. The signal lanterns of Newman and Pulling have sparked this change to come, but for now, Ben can continue to rest. The night of April 18-19, 1775, is still young.

The Midnight Ride

Back at the waterfront, a major obstacle appears directly in the path of Paul Revere's safe passage by rowboat to Charlestown. The British warship HMS *Somerset* is anchored in the Charles River to prevent nighttime traffic between Boston and Charlestown. The full moon is unusually low on the horizon as Joshua Bentley, Thomas Richardson, and Paul Revere prepare for their journey. The position of the moon is to their advantage and should allow the small wooden rowboat to hide, at least partially, in the shadows. The sound of their oars scraping against the boat as they row, however, is another matter. Revere fears it is sure to give them away unless something can be done to muffle the noise.

Both of Revere's friends agree, and one of them dashes off in search of a solution. A few minutes later, he is back with what appears to be a woman's woolen undergarment. There is no time to ask where he found it. The men tear the garment in two, wrap both halves around the oar handles near the locks, and tie them off securely. A moment later, the men push off from the shore.

Bentley and Richardson carefully row Revere downstream, to the eastward side of the HMS *Somerset*. Even though they try to keep a safe distance from the ship, they still worry about being spotted. With every stroke, this concern grows larger. The men do not talk—they dare not risk it—but their eye contact speaks volumes. They pass by the position of the mighty ship, expecting that at any moment a distant voice will cry out from on board, and their mission will be discovered. By this time, Newman and Pulling had sent the signal, and Paul Revere is anxious to discover if the message has been received in Charlestown. The men row on, beyond the HMS *Somerset*, and to their great relief, remain undetected. Soon, they reach their landing point near the Charlestown Battery.

Once ashore, Revere walks into town and meets with local members of the Sons of Liberty who had been expecting him. He informs Colonel William Conant about the events in Boston and learns that the signal from the steeple of Christ Church was seen. Richard Devens, a member of the Committee of Safety, tells Revere that British patrols were spotted earlier in the evening and warns him to watch out for them. Paul Revere borrows a very good horse from John Larkin and sets out toward Lexington. The time is 11 p.m.

Just an hour before, the King's troops were beginning to gather for their march. General Thomas Gage had ordered this expedition, and over 700 of his Regulars had marched to an isolated stretch of beach at the foot of Boston Common, on the edge of Back Bay. As Revere rides off toward Lexington, these troops, under the command of Colonel Francis Smith, are being transported by rowboat across Back Bay to a beach on Lechmere Point in Cambridge. Colonel Smith's troops are composed of Grenadiers and light infantry. Twenty-one companies are represented. At 11 p.m., only half of his troops have landed in Cambridge and the boats are returning for the balance of his men.

By 11:15 p.m., Paul Revere has traveled across Charlestown Neck on the Larkin family horse. Now he approaches a crossroads. To his right, the road meanders along the Mystic River toward Medford. To his left, the road leads to Cambridge. Revere chooses the left road, which is the fastest route to Lexington. As he crosses Charlestown Common and heads toward Cambridge, he spots two British officers on horseback near a tree in a narrow part of the road. As one of the figures moves in his direction, Revere turns his horse sharply and, at a full gallop, makes for the Mystic Road. The officer gives chase, but after about 300 yards, Revere's horse proves faster. The officer's mount becomes stuck in a clay pond and Paul Revere escapes the patrol.

The new route means that Revere's trip to Lexington will now cover 12 miles. Just ahead, he crosses a small bridge over the Mystic River and enters the village of Medford. Here he awakes the captain of the Minutemen and delivers the news of the Regulars' movements. Paul Revere continues his ride over a dark, rutted, dirt road that takes him back across the river and to the town of Menotomy. From here, he continues to awake almost every house along his path with a knock at the door and a brief message of warning. Next, Paul Revere, a 40-year-old Boston silversmith, turns onto the Great Road and rides on through the night toward Lexington.

Around midnight, Colonel Smith's troops are all safely across Back Bay and gathered at Lechmere Point in Cambridge. When their boats came ashore in the shallow bay, the men had walked through water that was almost waist high. On a chilly evening, this was both unexpected and unwelcome. As his men begin to get their bearings, Colonel Smith realizes that they have landed in swamp and marshland. The closest property to them is called Phipp's Farm. The muddy footing is terrible, the wet men are freezing, and Colonel Smith now orders them to wait here for a ship that will bring them two days' provisions of food for their expedition.

At midnight, Paul Revere, having escaped from one British patrol and carried the warning to nearly every darkened farmhouse on his route, has now reached his objective: Lexington. He rides past the town's meeting house on Lexington Common and approaches Buckman Tavern. A short distance beyond, Revere reaches the parsonage of Reverend Jonas Clarke. Reverend Clarke and members of his family are asleep inside, as are his guests, Samuel Adams, John Hancock, Dorothy Quincy (Hancock's fiancée), and Lydia Hancock (his aunt).

The house is guarded by Sergeant William Munroe and other members of the Lexington militia. As Revere's horse approaches and his voice rings out, Sergeant Munroe cautions him to be quiet. The family has gone to bed and does not wish to be disturbed.

An irritated Revere replies, "Noise! You'll have noise enough before long! The Regulars are coming out!"

Hearing the commotion, Reverend Clarke opens his bedroom window and sticks his head outside. A moment later, John Hancock, recognizing Revere's voice, asks him to come inside. Revere asks about the other messenger rider sent by Dr. Joseph Warren and learns that William Dawes has not yet arrived. He informs Adams and Hancock of the British march and expresses concern for their safety.

At 12:30 a.m., William Dawes arrives at the parsonage. He had made his way successfully past the British guards on Boston Neck. His route, entirely by land, was four miles longer than Revere's. Inside the Clarke house, Dawes and Revere "refresh" themselves and decide to continue on to Concord, which is six miles away. On the road to Concord, Paul Revere and William Dawes are overtaken by a lone rider, Dr. Samuel Prescott of Concord. The Doctor, who had been courting a young woman in Lexington, was on his way home for the evening. Once informed of the important news, he decides to join the men and help spread the alarm.

After 1 a.m., a British patrol stops the men. Dawes and Prescott escape, but Revere is captured. After the officers learn the name of the well-known messenger rider, Major Edward Mitchell of the 5th Regiment of Foot holds a pistol to Revere's head and questions him. He learns that Revere has alarmed the country all the way from Boston. The patrol takes Revere and four other prisoners they had captured earlier, back toward Lexington.

Soon, shots ring out in the distance. The officers become frightened and decide to release four of their prisoners. As they approach the Lexington Meeting House, more shots can be heard. The officers release Revere as well. At 2 a.m., Paul Revere is set free, but his horse is taken by one of the British officers. He makes his way across a burying ground and a pasture and finally back to the Clarke house. He is surprised to discover that Samuel Adams and John Hancock are still there. After much discussion, Adams and Hancock decide to flee to Woburn, and Revere travels with them. Along the way, John Hancock becomes concerned about some papers he left in his trunk at Buckman Tavern. Revere and Hancock's clerk, John Lowell, offer to retrieve the trunk.

By 2 a.m., Colonel Smith's British Regulars finally receive their provisions and begin their march. They reach Menotomy at 3 a.m. Here, Colonel Smith gives his men a brief rest. The delay in Cambridge has cost valuable time, and dawn is not far off. The Colonel becomes concerned that there might be more trouble than he has expected. He decides to send a message back to Lord Percy, calling for his 1,000 reinforcements. Next, Colonel Smith calls for his second in command, Major John Pitcairn of the Marines. He orders Pitcairn to take six companies ahead to Concord at the quickest possible pace. Their route will take them through the town of Lexington.

By 4:30 a.m., Paul Revere and John Lowell are back in Lexington at Buckman Tavern to retrieve John Hancock's trunk. Major Pitcairn and his six companies are fast approaching. John Parker, Captain of the Lexington militia, calls out to his 19-year-old drummer, William Diamond, "Billy, beat the call to arms!" Members of the militia heed the call and race out of Buckman Tavern and the surrounding buildings. They form ranks near Captain Parker on Lexington Common. Tension fills the air as this small band of farmers stand their ground and prepare to face hundreds of soldiers from the world's most powerful army.

Lexington and Concord

In the early morning light, from a window on the second floor of Buckman Tavern, Paul Revere and John Lowell can see Major Pitcairn's British Regulars nearing Lexington Common. The two men have located John Hancock's trunk, which is filled with his valuable papers. They now must move it to a safe location before the King's troops reach them.

Revere and Lowell lift the heavy trunk and carry it down the narrow stairs and out the front entrance of Buckman Tavern. They make their way across the north end of the Common and pass directly through the ranks of Captain Parker's Lexington militia, about 70 militiamen who anxiously await instructions from their leader. As he passes these men, Paul Revere hears Captain Parker's words, "Let the troops pass by, don't molest them without they being first."

Revere and Lowell struggle across the Common with Hancock's trunk and, at the far end, cross a road and head toward a section of trees just beyond a house. On the Common itself, Captain Parker's instructions continue, "Stand your ground. Don't fire unless fired upon, but if they mean to have a war, let it begin here." Two of Major Pitcairn's six companies now march straight toward the militia.

At the front of the column are several British officers on horseback. One of them cries out, "Disperse ye rebels, disperse!" while another demands, "Lay down your arms!"

The infantry behind these mounted officers begins to form a battle line. Their muskets are already loaded with powder and ball. Before the militia can be surrounded by a much larger force, Captain Parker revises his orders and now tells his men to "disperse and not to fire." There is much noise and confusion, but most of the men hear his command and begin to give ground.

At this moment, from his vantage point at the far end of the Common, Paul Revere hears what sounds like a pistol shot. He turns and sees a patch of smoke in front of the Regulars. His view of the militia is blocked by a building. A moment later Revere hears a full volley and then a continual roar of musketry.

The British musket balls find their targets. Two of Captain Parker's militiamen, Jonas Parker and Robert Munroe, are killed where they stand, and six others are mortally wounded as they retreat. It is an awful scene. One of the wounded, Jonathan Harrington, crawls toward his home, which is located on the west side of the Common. Here, he dies on his front doorstep. Another, young Isaac Muzzy, dies at his father's feet. This is one of five pairs of fathers and sons who will suffer a similar loss on this early April morning. Ten other members of the militia also receive wounds, some severe.

As for the British Regulars, only one member of the infantry is hit. He receives a wound to the leg. Major Pitcairn's horse is also hit with two musket balls.

A short time later, British Colonel Francis Smith arrives on the scene with his main force. The dead and wounded litter the field. Colonel Smith is dismayed by what he sees. Finding Pitcairn's men disorganized, he takes immediate action. Smith orders his drummer to beat "to arms," and his men slowly gather up on the Common. The Colonel then gathers together his officers and tells them the objective of their expedition. They will continue their march for six more miles until they reach Concord. Here they will seek out and destroy the Colony's store of gunpowder and muskets. His officers express concern. After what has just occurred, they are certain that the militia at Concord will be expecting them. Smith tells them he is determined to carry on with the mission, which had been ordered by General Gage.

Before they leave the field, Colonel Smith allows his men to fire a victory salute. Hundreds of muskets fire into the air, and the Regulars give three cheers as they continue their march to Concord.

Members of the Lexington militia who lie hidden in the woods and surrounding buildings hear this celebration. Remembering those who have just fallen, they vow that the Colonel and his men have not seen the last of them on this day.

Back in Boston, 10-year-old Ben Edwards awakes to the crow of a friendly rooster just outside his bedroom window. It is just past 7 a.m. on this Wednesday morning, April 19, 1775. Ben sits on the edge of his small bed and hears someone making noise in the kitchen. It is his Aunt Sarah. Up since dawn, she is busy preparing the morning meal. As Ben rubs the sleep from his eyes, he wanders into the kitchen.

"Good morning Ben," says Aunt Sarah. "You look like you haven't slept a wink."

"I couldn't fall asleep," responds Ben. "I went outside last night and looked up at the sky through my spyglass. I saw something strange, Aunt Sarah. Thirteen stars appeared in the shape of a circle in the night sky. Why would there be 13?"

Aunt Sarah, believing Ben had imagined the incident, offers the quickest explanation she can think of.

"Why, that's one for each of the 13 colonies, Ben. Now eat the food I've made and soon you'll be off to the shop with your uncle."

Ben considers his aunt's response as he eats his breakfast. Fifteen minutes later, his Uncle Alex enters from outside. Up since 6 a.m., he has been out on an early errand.

Turning to his wife, he says, "Just as we expected, Sarah. The Sons say that the Regulars marched last night from the Common and were taken by boat to Cambridge. To what end it is not known, but I expect word will come soon."

Uncle Alex's face has that look of concern that Ben noticed earlier in the week. This time, he is afraid to think what it might mean.

Beyond Lexington Common, in the town of Concord, it is now nearing 8 a.m., and Colonel Smith's British troops are just about to arrive. The militia here was alerted by Dr. Samuel Prescott around 1 a.m., and they are preparing for the Regulars' approach. The militia's commander is Colonel James Barrett, a 65-year-old veteran of the French and Indian War. He has mustered two Minutemen companies and two militia companies in front of Wright's Tavern. A rider has just delivered a firsthand account of the battle at Lexington. Colonel Barrett orders his men to position themselves along a high ridge overlooking Concord Road. He sends another company directly down that same road, hoping to deter the Regular's advance.

Meanwhile, Colonel Smith's troops are not about to be stopped by a few companies of Yankee militia. As the British approach in force, Colonel Barrett has the Colonists draw back. He is not yet ready to do battle. When the Regulars reach Concord, Colonel Smith sends one company to guard the South Bridge over the Concord River and the balance of his men to the North Bridge. Four of these companies cross the river and head toward Colonel Barrett's farm, which is two miles away, in search of a store of gunpowder and weapons. At the same time, the Grenadiers, who are searching the town for supplies and weapons, finally find a few items in the courthouse. They pile these items in the street and set them ablaze.

From his position on the ridge, smoke is now visible from Concord center, and Colonel Barrett worries that the Regulars might decide to burn the town. He decides to send his men back into Concord to protect their homes and families. To get there, they will have to cross the North Bridge, which is now guarded by 120 members of British infantry. By now the militia's numbers exceed 400 men. They make their way down from the ridge and march toward the North Bridge. The men are led by 30-year-old Captain Isaac Davis.

The British at the North Bridge are commanded by Captain Walter Laurie. He tells his men they must hold the bridge or the four companies that set out earlier for Barrett's farm may be cut off. It is 10 a.m. when the militia reaches the bridge. Several of the Regulars on the opposite side fire a warning shot to halt them. The militia continues its advance.

A moment later, the British troops fire a full volley into the center of the militia line. Captain Davis falls with a bullet in his chest, and Abner Hosmer is also mortally wounded.

Four other members of the militia are also hit. The brave men do not falter. They fire into the British line. Two privates are killed, and nine more men, including four officers, are wounded. In a matter of minutes, the Regulars are broken, and they retreat from the bridge.

Colonel Smith gathers his men and his four companies manage to return safely from Barrett's farm. He retreats to the center of Concord. Here he waits, hoping that reinforcements will arrive. From a hill above the Concord burying ground, he and Major Pitcairn look down the long road to Lexington, searching for any sign of Lord Percy and his 1,000 troops. What they see instead are many Minutemen and militia from surrounding towns making their way toward that same road to do battle with the British force as they return through Lexington.

Word of the fighting at Lexington reaches Boston just a few hours after young Ben finished his morning meal. Shortly after 10 a.m., Thomas Sherburne enters the cabinetmaking shop with the news. Ben listens intently as he speaks.

"Shots have been fired at Lexington, near the Common. Members of the militia were killed. Many others wounded." Earlier in the morning, Uncle Alex sensed something like this might occur. For his nephew's benefit, he holds his anger in check but speaks firmly and plainly.

"Well, Thomas, the war for liberty has surely begun, and I have some business to attend to." Uncle Alex sends Ben home at noon and tells him not to worry his aunt with the news.

By noon, in Concord, no reinforcements have arrived, and Colonel Smith decides to begin the march back to Boston. A 19-mile running battle soon follows between his troops and some 1,500 Minutemen and militia. The Minutemen and militia ambush the half-mile-long column of marching British soldiers from behind trees, stone walls, and farm buildings. The Regulars send out flanking parties on both sides of the narrow road as they limp their way back. When Colonel Smith's men cross the Lexington line, Captain Parker's Lexington militia are hiding in the woods nearby. As the Regulars cross a small bridge, the militia opens fire. In this volley, Colonel Smith is shot in the thigh, and he falls from his mount. Major Pitcairn replaces him at the head of the column, and he orders the Grenadiers to attack Parker's men. After some fierce fighting, the Lexington men retreat.

As the desperate battle continues, the British column approaches the east side of Lexington Common. Finally, at 2 p.m., they see Lord Percy and his reinforcements marching in their direction. Even with the approach of the British reinforcements, the Minutemen and militia continue to battle the Regulars. The fighting continues into the afternoon as Major Pitcairn and his men attempt to make their way back to Charlestown.

At 2:30 p.m., Ben is at the Edwards home on Back Street. He has been there for several hours. The news from Lexington has spread quickly through the town. Aunt Sarah can no longer hide it from the children. She gathers them in the kitchen to tell them what she knows. Before his aunt even speaks, Ben knows what she is going to say.

"Now I don't want you to be frightened," says Aunt Sarah, "but I've learned there's been some fighting near Lexington and the Regular troops fired on the militia there. I believe some members of the militia were badly wounded. Your uncle may know more when he returns from the shop in a few hours. For now, that is all I know, and I wanted you to hear it from me first."

Sally asks, "Why would the King's troops fire on their own people?" and then she adds, "that doesn't make sense, Aunt Sarah."

"I don't know the answer, Sally," replies Aunt Sarah. "Nothing about this occupation of Boston by the King's soldiers has ever made sense to me, and, sadly, I'm not surprised that it has come to this end. I do fear most that things may get worse."

On that note, Cousin Betsey races from the room while the other children appear surprised and concerned by the terrible news.

A short time later, Ben spots his cousin from a back window. She is sitting alone on the shore of the Mill Pond. The two 10-year-olds share a special bond. Betsey truly believes that one day Ben will work on a sailing ship. She encourages him at every opportunity. Ben loves his cousin and is always there when she needs someone to talk to. He feels that this is one of those times.

Ben walks outside, past the barn in back of the house, and takes a seat on the ground beside her. He notices that she is crying.

"Betsey, what's wrong?"

"There's going to be a war, Ben, I just know it, and Uncle Alex will have to fight, and maybe he will die. I can't bear to lose him, too!"

Ben puts his arm around his cousin, and the two orphans console one another.

"I know how you feel," he responds.

Aunt Sarah

Through her tears, Betsey continues, "I need to know how everything will turn out. Will Uncle Alex and Aunt Sarah always be here for us? What will become of me? Will I be happy, Ben? Will I have a family of my own? I know if you look into your spyglass, you can find the answer for me."

Betsey is the only other person who believes that Ben can see the future through his spyglass. She not only believes it, she is certain of it. Ben believes, too, but he has only seen a glimpse of his own future through it. He mainly sees images of larger events that he can't quite explain. However, to make his cousin Betsey feel better, he is willing to give it a try.

He turns to Betsey and says, "Every time I look through the spyglass from now on, I'll be looking for you."

As Ben wipes away the last tear from his cousin's eye, Betsey responds, "I hope you find me, Ben. I hope you find my future."

Later in the evening, Ben takes Betsey outside to look at the night sky through his spyglass. He hopes to see the circle of 13 stars he noticed the previous night. Through the lens, Ben sees what looks like a star falling from the sky.

"Ben, look!" cries Betsey. She points toward the streaking light. "What is it?"

Ben drops his spyglass, grabs Betsey's hand, and points toward the sky.

"I'm not sure," he says. "I've never seen anything like it before!" The light moves quickly toward the horizon and disappears.

"Could it have anything to do with the future?" asks Betsey.

"It could," says Ben.

"My future?" she asks with anticipation.

"I don't think so," he says. "I don't think it has anything to do with my future either. Maybe it's in our family's future." Ben pauses for a moment, then adds, "Now I wonder where that would be?"

Betsey looks disappointed, but her face brightens when she says, "I wish I could see where it landed!"

"So do I," says Ben, with a big smile. "So do I."

Independence

By the morning of April 20, casualty figures from the recent engagements at Lexington, Concord, and the fighting along the road to Charlestown are becoming known. British losses total 73 killed and 174 wounded. American losses amount to some 50 killed and 39 wounded. Cousin Betsey has sensed what the people in Boston are now beginning to say: "This means war."

Paul Revere delivered the alarm to Lexington and safely retrieved John Hancock's trunk. Now he faces a new predicament. He cannot return to Boston for fear of being arrested by the British. Sexton Robert Newman will be jailed shortly for his suspected involvement in the events of April 18 at Christ Church. Fearing a similar fate, Newman's associate and young Ben's friend, John Pulling, avoids pursuing soldiers by hiding in a wine barrel at his mother's home. He will soon escape Boston disguised as a mariner.

In nearby Charlestown, Paul Revere writes a quick letter to his wife, Rachel, letting her know he is safe and asking that she and the children join him when they can. He also asks her to leave their 15-year-old son, Paul Jr., behind to guard the family's property. Revere senses that British soldiers will be looking for firewood and food and an empty house will be an open invitation to them.

On May 3, 1775, Rachel and the children leave Boston. Paul Jr. is left behind for a time to fulfill his father's request. During this period, young Paul has to learn to cook for himself, a task normally handled by his mother and many sisters.

Over the next few weeks, Sally Edwards spots Paul Jr. sitting alone during church services. She becomes aware of his situation and offers to cook for him. He gladly accepts her offer, and their friendship grows. Neither Sally nor Paul could imagine it, but, in the future, they would be separated by war when young Paul and his father become soldiers in a newly formed army.

Shocked by the news of Lexington and Concord, the Continental Congress assembles in Philadelphia on May 10, 1775. This is the second meeting for this distinguished group of Colonial leaders and their most important. It is becoming clear that a national army is needed. The leaders must select the proper commander for such an army. Standing in the wings in the Pennsylvania State House is a 6-ft. 2-inch delegate from Virginia wearing his state's colorful militia uniform. He is 43-year-old Colonel George Washington. John Adams nominates Washington, and Adams's cousin, Samuel Adams, seconds the nomination. After some debate, Colonel Washington is elected Commander in Chief of the Continental Army. He will take command of a group of poorly trained troops at Cambridge, Massachusetts, on July 3, 1775. The first major battle, however, occurs near Boston before this date.

On June 17, 1775, two thousand British soldiers attack an impressive earthwork fort created by American troops on

Breed's Hill overlooking Charlestown. Young Ben is at work in the cabinetmaking shop when he and his Uncle Alex hear word of the battle. They leave the shop and, from a rooftop, they watch the British attack. It is a terribly hot day with temperatures well into the nineties. The American regiments atop Breed's Hill total nearly 1,500 men. British troops advance uphill toward the American position and are turned back twice. During a third assault, the defenders' ammunition finally runs out, and the British and Americans fight hand-to-hand, with the British using bayonets. The fighting is furious, and the British overtake the Americans.

Paul Revere's good friend Dr. Joseph Warren is killed. Although he held the rank of major general, Warren had fought this day as an ordinary private and had given his life in the cause for freedom. On the British side, Major John Pitcairn is wounded in the chest and carried off the field by his son. He later dies from his injuries. The British Regulars win the battle, but the cost is enormous. One third of their troops, including many officers, are either killed or wounded. The engagement is soon misnamed after a nearby landmark and called the Battle of Bunker Hill. Bunker Hill is slightly higher and immediately behind Breed's Hill.

In August of 1775, a group of Bostonians loyal to King George who were called "Tories" and their British friends direct their anger and hostility toward one of the town's most recognized symbols of liberty. Armed with axes, they cut down Boston's Liberty Tree. In the process they pay a high price. A British soldier who is attempting to remove a limb falls to the ground and is killed. When they are finished, the beautiful elm has been turned into 14 cords of firewood. Uncle Alex is normally an even-tempered man, but when he learns the news, he flies into a rage. Young Ben can never recall seeing his uncle so angry.

The tree had been planted in 1646 and was nearly 130 years old when it was cut down. It became known as Liberty Tree shortly after the newly formed Sons of Liberty used it to make a public protest of the Stamp Act on August 14, 1765. On that day, a dummy of stamp commissioner Andrew Oliver dangled from a noose on the tree's branches. Oliver later resigned from his duties as stamp master beneath the boughs of this same tree. Every August 14, the Sons of Liberty had gathered there to celebrate the anniversary of the Stamp Act protest. In August of 1767, a flag pole had been erected at Liberty Tree, passing through and above its highest branches. A flag flying from this location had been the signal for assembling the members. Even though a stump was all that remained of Liberty Tree, the fight for liberty would continue.

For the balance of 1775, Ben attends to his tasks as an apprentice. He is now becoming skillful with the planes, saws, and drawknives his uncle has taught him to use. He continues through a bitter winter and into spring of the new year. During this time, Ben keeps his promise and each day, reviews the goals he wrote earlier on the piece of paper he keeps beneath his bed.

In March of 1776, there is reason to celebrate. General Washington has taken Dorchester Heights, an area overlooking the town. His cannon, captured at Fort Ticonderoga, are pointed directly at the British Fleet anchored in the harbor. This is the turning point of the war around Boston. The British evacuate and sail toward Halifax, Nova Scotia.

Paul Revere Jr.

Sally Edwards

Independence

On July 17, 1776, Ben and his uncle take the horse-drawn wagon on a delivery. That afternoon, they stop briefly at Copp's Hill. As Uncle Alex makes a few repairs on the family tomb, Ben recalls the marker his uncle had shown him during a previous visit. He remembers the exact location of the stone. It is the marker for Capt. Daniel Malcom, "buried in a Stone Grave 10 feet deep ... a true son of Liberty." As he approaches it, Ben is surprised by what he sees.

"Uncle Alex, come look," Ben cries. As his uncle approaches, Ben's fingers trace over the stone. He thinks, "These weren't here last April."

"Those are musket ball marks," says his uncle, "surely made by the King's troops. The Regulars may be gone, Ben, but in their wake they've destroyed our property and scarred our town."

Those scars are evident all around Boston. The British had torn down the Old North Meeting House and many homes and buildings, and used them for firewood. They had removed the pews from the Old South Meeting House and burned them. The British used the inside of this building as a riding school. They left poor sanitary conditions in their wake, and there is fear of another smallpox epidemic.

On the afternoon of July 18, Uncle Alex has made plans to attend a gathering near Dock Square. He feels it will be an event of great importance and surely one that his young nephew should see. Ben is always excited to go places with his uncle and very agreeable to the invitation.

As the two begin to walk toward Dock Square, Ben's cousin Betsey races out of the Edwards home and follows them. She yells out to her cousin, "You forgot this, Ben!" Betsey runs up to him with his spyglass.

"Thanks, Betsey," says Ben.

Betsey turns to Uncle Alex and says, "Can I come, too, Uncle Alex?"

Her uncle smiles and responds, "Surely you can."

When they arrive at Dock Square, they follow others down Shrimpton's Lane to King Street. A large crowd is assembled here near the Town House.

Young Ben grows excited. He says, "Uncle, what is happening?"

Betsey, surrounded by people, calls out above the noise, "Uncle, I can't see anything."

Uncle Alex lifts her above the crowd and comments, "My dear Betsey, you're not as light as you used to be."

Then, from the second floor of the Town House, a door swings open, and Colonel Thomas Crafts steps out onto the balcony. The enthusiastic crowd cheers. With a voice strong and loud, he begins to speak.

"Fellow citizens of Boston, I now read the recent declaration adopted by Congress in Philadelphia, July 4, 1776." The crowd roars as he continues. "The unanimous Declaration of the thirteen United States of America, When in the Course of human events, it becomes necessary for one people to dissolve the political bands which have connected them with another...."

Ben watches the events through the lens of his spyglass. He soon hears "We hold these truths to be self-evident, that all men are created equal, that they are endowed by their Creator with certain unalienable Rights, that among these are Life, Liberty, and the pursuit of Happiness."

As the reading continues, Ben notices a flag waving in the breeze above the Town House. It contains a circle of 13 stars in a blue field, surrounded by 13 alternating red and white stripes. No one else can see it but Ben. It is visible only through the lens of his spyglass. Had he seen this before? Could it be a future symbol for this new nation? Thirteen stars and stripes for the 13 United States?

As the final lines of the Declaration of Independence are being read, Ben gets one more vision through the lens of his spyglass. This one is not for his new country, but for his cousin. Betsey had been patient as she waited for clues about her future. She would ask Ben each week, but he never had anything to tell her. How he hated to disappoint her. Now he had something. It didn't make sense, but that didn't matter. Betsey's future would be linked to the following three things: a tall man with whiskers, the number 16, and the name Lincoln. Ben is certain of it.

When the speech ends, the crowd erupts with applause and shouts of "God save our American States" fill the air. Artillery pieces fire, bells ring, and there is a great celebration. Uncle Alex lowers Betsey to the ground, and Ben tells her about her future. Later this day, the royal symbols of the lion and unicorn are removed from the Town House and burned in a bonfire in Dock Square. King Street will soon be renamed State Street, and the Town House will be called the State House. For now, Uncle Alex gathers the children and explains what they have just seen. "Today is a glorious day!" he proclaims. "We have all witnessed the birth of freedom and the beginning of our new nation."

The children follow their uncle as the crowd begins to leave.

On the way home, Betsey holds out her hands and says, "I'm tired, Uncle Alex. Can you pick me up?" Alexander reaches down and elevates his 10-year-old niece to a safe perch on his broad shoulders. Betsey asks, "Am I too heavy, Uncle?"

Alexander pauses for a moment and then responds, "Betsey, you'll never be too heavy for me to carry."

Betsey smiles and then whispers, "I love you, Uncle."

On they walk through the cobblestone streets of Boston, Ben clutching his spyglass and Betsey clutching her Uncle Alex. In a matter of moments, all three disappear around a bend in the road.

The Future

The Revolutionary War rages on for six more years. General Washington's strategic escape after the Battle of Long Island in August of 1776, and his stunning victory at Trenton on December 26, 1776 (after crossing the Delaware River with his army on Christmas evening), give the American troops hope as they face the many challenges that lie ahead. In 1777, the American victory at the Battle of Saratoga is a major turning point. The French now see that the new nation can succeed in fighting the British.

The American army suffers terribly through a bitter winter at Valley Forge in 1778, but their commitment to the ideals of liberty and self-government do not falter. The French sign an alliance with the Americans on February 6, 1778 and intervene to help the American cause.

On October 19, 1781, Lord Cornwallis surrenders to Generals Washington and Rochambeau at Yorktown, Virginia. Two years later, the Treaty of Paris is signed, and the dream of American independence is realized. The cost for independence is high. Of the 200,000 men who served in the army and militia at some point during the war, nearly 25,000 lost their lives!

There are no existing records to indicate whether Alexander Edwards fought in the Continental Army during the American Revolution. There are, however, many clues that tell us he was a wonderful uncle, father figure, and role model for his nine nieces and nephews. When these children had nowhere else to turn, Alexander and Sarah took them in and loved and raised them like their very own. Alexander lived to see all his children grow well into adulthood. He died of yellow fever on September 24, 1798, at the age of 64. His wife, Sarah, survived him.

Ben's sister Sally was married soon after the fighting ended. Her cousin Rebecca stood by her on that day, grinning from ear to ear. The groom was that fine young gentleman she had introduced Sally to one Sunday morning in April 1775, Paul Revere Jr. The wedding took place on July 25, 1782, as Paul Revere, his wife Rachel, Alexander Edwards, and his wife Sarah looked on.

As the years passed, Rebecca had even more reason to smile as the other predictions she made that Sunday morning in April also came true. Paul Jr. and Sally had 12 children! During this time, Paul Jr. ran the day-to-day operations of his father's silversmith shop and eventually manufactured church bells as a member of Paul Revere & Sons. When their first son was born on September 13, 1784, Sally and Paul Jr. recalled the name that Rebecca had suggested the day they met in the New Brick Church. Both agreed it would be a fine name and a fine tribute to someone they both admired. A few days after the birth, Paul Revere Jr. held up his young son and, in a proud voice, said, "Alexander Edwards Revere, welcome to Boston." Rebecca Edwards, the likeable young instigator of the Edwards family, was married several years after her cousin Sally. Her husband was Caleb Coolidge.

For years, Ben's cousin Betsey looked for the clues he had given her about her future: a tall man with whiskers, the number 16, and the name Lincoln. One summer day near the family home on Back Street, she met an intelligent young carpenter. For Betsey, it was love at first sight. When she learned his name, she nearly fainted. It was Jedediah Lincoln. They courted for over a year and were married on October 27, 1785.

Betsey and Jedediah had six children. She, too, named her firstborn son after her beloved Uncle Alex. Alexander Edwards Lincoln was born on July 12, 1786. Betsey never failed to tease her cousin Ben about the three clues he had given her that never came to pass. Although his name was Lincoln, Jedediah was not a tall man, and he was never inclined to grow whiskers. As for the number 16 that Ben had seen through his spyglass, that never quite made sense either.

Ben would be proven correct some 70 years later, long after he and his cousin Betsey had died. It was then that the vision he saw on that July afternoon in Boston finally made sense. In the year 1861, a tall man with whiskers, who also happened to be a relative of Jedediah Lincoln, became the 16th President of the United States. His name was Abraham Lincoln. It was his vision for the young nation that predicted "a new birth of freedom."

Ben Edwards, the 10-year-old boy who loved the ocean and sailing ships, became a cooper in Boston and spent his time making barrels near the wharves. The cabinetmaking trade was better suited for his younger brother Alexander, who followed in his uncle's footsteps. Ben never forgot the lessons he learned from his Uncle Alex. He married Mary (Polly) Bangs on June

22, 1791. They had five children. Ben named his firstborn son Benjamin Edwards, after his grandfather, the mariner. He became a cooper, like his father. Ben's second son was named Alexander. He became a blacksmith. The couple also had two daughters, Bathsheba and Maryan, and a third son, Joseph Bragdon Edwards, who was born on December 29, 1799.

Early copies of the Boston City Directory list Ben as a cooper on Back Street and Ship Street. For a few years during this period, there are no listings for him. It is during this time we believe he finally realized his dream and worked as a cooper aboard sailing vessels departing from Boston Harbor. He may have taken his spyglass with him on these voyages as he continued his lifelong search for glimpses of the future. Ben died on June 9, 1808.

According to family legend, the spyglass was passed on to his son, Joseph B. Edwards. Joseph was employed as a paver in Boston, and he was also an innkeeper. City records from 1850 indicate that his household consisted of Joseph B., his wife, Sarah, two children, 20-year-old Mary Minahin of Ireland, and 15 persons with different last names, ages, and birthplaces.

Joseph died in 1852. The family eventually moved from Boston and soon settled in two Connecticut towns, East Haddam and Naugatuck. Joseph's son, Benjamin, took the spyglass along. He gave it to his 10-year-old grandson, Philip, in 1905. Young Phil was captivated by his 70-year-old grandfather's tales of the American Revolution, the Civil War, and Abraham Lincoln, whom he had voted for twice. He also told Phil stories about his ancestor Ben, a cooper in Boston who dreamed of working on sailing ships and traveling to distant shores. Phil learned that through hard work and persistence, Ben reached his goal and made his dream come true.

Young Phil loved his grandpa's stories, and he even kept pictures of Abe Lincoln and sailing ships in his room. In the summer of 1905, Phil began to get visions of his own through his ancestor's spyglass. For the most part, he kept these visions to himself, but one morning in July, he decided to share a few of them with two of his closest friends.

Millville

July 1905

On Saturday morning, July 15, 1905, not a single cloud is visible in the sky. It is the beginning of a glorious summer day. Ten-year-old Philip Edwards sits in his usual spot on the front steps of the family home. The small wooden house is located in the Millville section of Naugatuck, Connecticut. In his left hand, Phil holds his fishing pole, and in his right hand, he grasps his spyglass. The time is 8:30 a.m., and Phil awaits the arrival of his fishing buddies, John Simmons and Warren Birdsall. He peers down the dirt road in front of his house, which leads toward the center of town. John and Warren will be coming from that direction soon. The road is appropriately named "Rubber Avenue," as the town of Naugatuck is well known for its production of rubber goods.

As Phil waits anxiously for his friends, his father, Ben, steps out the front door and onto the porch.

"A fine day for fishing, Phil," he says. "I'm off to the company for a few hours this morning. Next Saturday I'll go along with you and your friends. If you use the boat today, remember to leave it where you found it after you're done."

"I will, Dad," says Phil.

In the distance, Phil sees his friends approaching with fishing poles in their hands. As 37-year-old Ben Edwards heads down the street toward them, two loud voices call out.

"Good morning, Mr. E.," says Warren.

"Good morning, Dad!" cries John.

John Simmons considers Phil's folks his second family, which is why he calls Phil's father, "Dad."

Ben Edwards responds, "Good morning, boys. I wish I could be going with you today, but I'm off to work at the Rubber Company. Those bass in Long Meadow Pond just keep getting bigger every year. Promise you'll leave a few behind for me to catch next weekend."

"We'll leave one or two for you, Dad," says John. "My father is working today, too," he adds.

"So is mine," says Warren.

Warren Birdsall Sr. and George Washington Simmons work with Phil's dad at one of the town's largest employers, The Goodyear Metallic Rubber Shoe Company.

As Ben Edwards walks toward work, John and Warren greet Phil at the Edwards home.

"Are you ready to catch some fish, Phil?" asks Warren.

"I sure am," says Phil. "What took you guys so long?"

"I had a few chores this morning," says John. "Let's get going!"

Long Meadow Pond is a 2-1/2-mile walk from the Edwards home. It is located in the neighboring town of Middlebury. The boys go fishing there nearly every weekend during the summer and fall. John and Warren are the same age as Phil. All three have been fishing companions for the last two years. Every Saturday, as they walk to the pond, something manages to distract them. Today is no exception.

As the boys stride up Rubber Avenue, they approach a landmark that is the basis of a local legend. On the right-hand side of the road is a large rock that stands over 12 ft. tall. Members of the community refer to it as the "star stone" and believe it is a meteor that fell to earth shortly after the area was first settled in 1765. Phil peers at the stone through his spyglass.

"Phil, you've seen that rock a hundred times before," says John. "Do you have to stare at it through that spyglass every time we go fishing?"

"There's just something about it that interests me," says Phil. "I really can't explain it. I'll bet it landed here when my great-great-grandfather Ben was alive. He was born in Boston in 1765. Just think, I'm looking at it through his spyglass!"

"How do you know that spyglass really belonged to him?" asks Warren.

"I think it did," says Phil, "at least my grandpa says it was his. I think all of Grandpa's stories are true."

"Like that story about Paul Revere?" asks Warren, "how you're related to him somehow. Maybe through his horse!!"

John laughs.

"Very funny," says Phil. "Grandpa said my great-great-grandfather Ben's sister married one of Paul Revere's sons, but I guess you guys are right. I really have no proof of that either. Maybe someday I'll be able to prove it to you. Until then, all I have are Grandpa's stories and this spyglass."

For a moment, Phil thinks about telling John and Warren about the recent glimpses he has seen through the spyglass, but he decides to wait until a bit later when they are all out in the boat.

Further up on Rubber Avenue, the boys near the Elliott Farm. Eight-year-old Ethel Elliott stands in the yard and notices the boys approaching.

"I thought I'd see the 'fisher boys' today," she says with a smile. "Come over here, John Simmons, I need to ask you a favor."

John goes over to speak with Ethel. They talk for quite a while, and Phil and Warren start to get anxious.

"Come on, John," says Warren. "We're going fishing today, not courting!"

"I'll be right there," shouts John.

When John returns, Warren says, "She likes you John. Every time we walk by that farmhouse, she makes up some excuse to speak with you. It's crazy! Why don't you just marry her. Then maybe we'll have a better chance of getting to the pond on time!"

"How about next Sunday?" asks John.

"What about it?" says Warren.

"The wedding could be next Sunday," he says.

"What!!" shouts Warren.

Phil grabs Warren by the shirt, shakes him, and says, "He's joking!"

"I knew that," says Warren. "Anyway, we'll be fishing all next weekend so there won't be time for any wedding. We'll just have to get up earlier so we can sneak by before Ethel spots us!"

"You've got to keep your mind off the girls, John," says Phil. "Remember, nothing is more important than fishing!"

John puts his arm around Phil and says, "One day, as hard as it is to believe, something will be more important to us than fishing. I'm not there yet, but when that day comes, I think I know what that something will be."

Phil shakes his head, then changes the subject in an instant. "Race you to the pond!" he shouts.

In a flash, the boys are off. They race up South Street and then turn left onto Long Meadow Road. This road goes directly to the pond. At the usual spot, they cut through the woods and hike to the location where Phil's dad keeps his boat hidden. They turn the boat over and drag it toward the pond. Once the boat is in the water, they pick up the oars, get in, and begin to row to their favorite spot.

"Ethel asked if we could do her a favor today," says John.

"What kind of favor?" asks Phil.

"The little five-year-old girl who lives down the street from her loves pond lilies. Her name is Ella Wininger. Ethel said that Ella asked if she could find some for her at Long Meadow Pond and bring them back so she could keep them in a bucket of water in her room. Ethel knew that we had a boat, and she asked if we could cut some today and drop them off at the Wininger house."

"We finally get on the water, and you want us to spend our time picking flowers?" asks Warren.

"They're not flowers, they're pond lilies," says John.

"Lilies are flowers, and I'm not picking any flowers. I'm here to catch the biggest fish."

"You mean the second biggest," says Phil.

"I've got an idea," says John. "What if we make a bet? Whoever is the worst fisherman of the day, whoever catches the least amount of fish, has to pick the pond lilies and deliver them to Ethel's friend."

Warren and Phil think for a moment. Each of them is confident that they will catch the biggest fish, but what about the most fish?

"What time would the contest end?" asks Phil.

"The time now is 10 a.m. Let's say we fish until 3 p.m. That would make the contest five hours long. Are you guys ready to start?"

Warren nods his head in agreement, and Phil adds, "I'm ready, John. I've got nothing to worry about. I have a feeling that today's my lucky day!"

As the contest begins, Phil feels it's time to tell his friends about the visions he has seen through his spyglass. Phil thinks this is necessary because those visions include images of John and Warren. He is worried that his buddies will laugh at him, but he just can't keep the information to himself any longer.

"Guys, there's something I need to talk to you about," says Phil.

"What's on your mind, pal?" replies John.

"It's about this spyglass I carry around all the time. My grandpa told me to keep this a secret, but I just can't do it any longer."

"Keep what a secret?" asks Warren.

"I know you're going to think this is crazy, but I see things through it that I can't explain. They seem to be clues about the future."

John, with a puzzled look on his face, says, "I'm listening, Phil. What kind of things do you see?"

"Last week I saw the image of a large ship with a British flag on it. On board that ship were men dressed in uniform. All of them were older, maybe in their 20s. As I looked closer, I noticed that two of those men were you and Warren. Both of you were speaking to another man whose back was toward me. As I continued to watch, that man slowly turned around. I soon realized that it was me, and then the vision disappeared."

"It sounds like you had a dream," says Warren.

"This was no dream," replies Phil. "I was wide awake. It was the second vision I received, a day later, that bothered me the most. This time I saw another ship with some of the same men on it. As I looked closer, once again, I spotted you and John on board. I searched and searched for the image of myself I had seen before, but could not find it. What do you make of it, John?"

"What kind of uniforms were the men wearing?" he asks.

"They looked like soldiers," says Phil.

"I'm not sure what it means, Phil, but I wouldn't be bothered by it. Are you positive it wasn't a dream?"

"As positive as I can be," says Phil.

"In case you're interested, guys," says Warren, "here's a look at the first fish of the day." Warren brings a nice bass into the boat. This one's about a foot long, but the size doesn't matter. It makes the score Warren, one, and John and Phil, zero. The fishing continues for several hours, and by 2:30 p.m., Warren has caught eight, John, seven, and Phil, five.

"Get ready to pick some lilies, Phil," says Warren as his fishing pole bends and nearly breaks. "This one makes nine." Soon another bass is flopping around in the boat. It is the largest fish of the day, 17 inches long! John soon catches his eighth fish, and now Phil is getting worried.

"Ten minutes left," says John.

As the minutes tick away, Phil manages to land one more fish, but it puts his total at only six.

"Time's up," says John. "It is now exactly 3 p.m., and time to do that favor for Ethel. The lucky guy who gets to do it is you, Phil!"

"That's just great," says Phil, with a frown on his face. "Well, row me over there and let's get this over with."

A cluster of pond lilies is growing a short distance away, about thirty yards from shore. John and Warren row Phil close to them, and he pulls his fishing knife from his pocket.

"Cut them well below the surface, and they'll last longer," says John.

"When did you become the flower expert?" says Phil with a smirk.

Phil leans over the side of the boat and reaches into the water. "How far down should I cut them, John?" he asks.

"Just a little lower," replies John.

Phil shifts closer to the side of the boat and reaches down further into the water. Suddenly, he loses his balance and lets out a scream. He tumbles head first into the pond, making a big splash. When he returns to the surface, a lily pad rests on top of his head. John and Warren are doubled over with laughter.

"You should be able to cut them low enough from there," says John.

"Thanks," replies Phil, as he removes the lily pad from his head. "After they're cut, I'll leave them with you guys and swim back."

Phil cuts four pond lilies with his fishing knife, drops them into the boat, and swims to shore. John and Warren row to the spot on the shore where they had found the boat earlier in the day. With Phil's help, they drag the wooden boat into the woods and turn it upside down, placing the oars underneath. The boys begin to walk back toward Millville. John and Warren carry all the fish, and Phil holds the pond lilies that he will deliver shortly.

"Where am I taking these, John?" he asks.

"To the Wininger house. We'll pass by it. It's just before the star stone."

"What's the little girl's name?"

"Ella. Ella Wininger."

"I hope she appreciates it," says Phil.

The boys soon reach the Wininger house. A man stands in the front yard as they approach. It is Ella's father, John Wininger.

"Looks like a successful day of fishing," he says. "All except for you, son. It looks like you caught more pond lilies than fish and fell in the water, too!"

"Well, sir, I lost a bet. Then I lost my balance, and, uh ... it's a long story. I just want to deliver these pond lilies to a little girl who lives here named Ella."

"That would be my daughter," says John. "Who can I say is delivering them?"

"Philip Edwards, sir, but you can call me 'Phil.'"

"I'll do that, Phil, and I'll have Ella come right out."

John calls for his daughter, who comes running down from her room on the second floor. When Ella sees the pond lilies, her big brown eyes grow wide. "Are those for me?" she asks with excitement.

"They sure are. Your friend Ethel asked us to get them for you." Phil introduces himself and his two friends.

Ella gives Phil an unexpected hug and then says, "You're all wet. Did you swim out to get them?"

"We have a boat," says Phil. "I'm just not very good at staying in it!"

Ella turns to her father and says, "Pa, can I put these in a bucket of water and keep them in my room, please, can I?"

"Sure, Ella," he says. "I'll help you do it. Thanks, boys. It looks like you've made my daughter very happy. Goodbye now."

Ella runs toward the house and then turns toward the street to see the boys walking away. "Thank you, Phil," she yells out and then dashes inside.

"Now that wasn't so bad, was it?" says John.

"I guess not," replies Phil.

"I think she even liked you," says John. He holds his fishing pole out and pretends to look through it. "I can see it through my spyglass now. The two of you get married in about 12 years and have a whole bunch of kids."

"John, that's not funny. First of all, she's only five, and second of all, you don't have a spyglass like mine. Trust me. You wouldn't want one, either."

"Through my spyglass, Phil, that's what I see. Believe me."

Phil shakes his head. "I've got to get out of these wet clothes before my mom catches me. She'll make me wash up on the spot."

The boys continue to walk down Rubber Avenue and soon return to the Edwards home. Phil's mother, Minnie, is sitting in a chair on the front porch. As Phil gets closer, she notices that he is wet.

"Did you boys go fishing or swimming?" she asks. "By the looks of it, I'd say Phil did a little of both. Hello, John. Hello, Warren. It's always good to see you boys. Why don't you stay and join us for dinner?"

"That sounds great, Mrs. E.," says Warren.

"I'd love to, Mother," replies John. "I eat over here more often than I eat at home. My mom is starting to worry that I don't like her cooking!"

Minnie Edwards smiles and sends Phil off to get washed up. As Phil cleans up in the next room, he yells out a question to his mother.

"Mom, is a pond lily a flower?"

Minnie gives the boys a strange look, and they all laugh.

The next few years in Millville go according to plan. Phil, John, and Warren attend school together, and each week, they count the days until the weekend. Every Saturday and most Sundays during the summer and fall, the "fisher boys," as Ethel calls them, walk the same route to Long Meadow Pond. Ethel always finds a reason to speak with John, no matter how hard Warren tries to keep their fishing plans on schedule. Eventually, Ethel convinces John to take her out in the boat.

In July of 1909, Ethel's nine-year-old friend, Ella Wininger, tags along, and Phil teaches her how to row. They joke about the first time they met, and Phil gathers a few pond lilies for her while somehow managing to stay dry. Ella has a wonderful smile and a great personality. She knows just what to say to make Phil laugh.

Phil continues to get visions through his spyglass, and he struggles to make sense of them. He also begins to wonder more about the stories his grandpa told him. Phil wants to know if these stories about his Boston ancestors are really true. In August of 1909, Phil takes a break from fishing and spends some time at his Grandpa Ben's farm in East Haddam, Connecticut. During this time, 14-year-old Phil asks his grandpa a few questions, and he receives a surprising answer.

Returning Home

"Grandpa, I love your stories about Ben the cooper and his Uncle Alex," says Phil. "The spyglass you gave me, did that really belong to Ben? Was he really my great-great-grandfather? Is there really an Old North Church? Where did Paul Revere live? Once you've answered those, I have 100 more questions."

"Phil, I'm happy you like my stories. I believe we can answer many of your questions by returning home for a few days."

"Returning home?" asks Phil. "Home to Naugatuck?"

Grandpa Ben laughs.

"Returning home to the place I left over 50 years ago. Why, returning home to Boston, of course."

Phil jumps up. "Can we really go to Boston? When, Grandpa, when? How would we get there?"

"Well, Phil, if I can convince your parents, we can go in a few weeks. I'll mail them a letter tomorrow asking for their permission. We could take the train from Waterbury to South Station in Boston. We'd be there in about four hours."

Phil is so excited. As if going to Boston isn't enough, he has never been on a train, either. This would be a real adventure.

"I hope you can convince my parents, Grandpa," says Phil, "I hope, I hope!"

Over the next ten days, Phil does his chores around the farm and dreams of a trip to Boston. He gathers eggs for his Grandma Mary and puts hay in the barn for the horses. Phil loves horses, and he loves the Edwards farm. On the evening of Thursday, August 19, Phil's grandma tells him that a letter arrived from his parents a few days earlier. His grandpa has been keeping it a secret. Grandpa Ben has a big smile on his face. Phil knows that smile can only mean one thing, "permission granted." He gives his grandfather a big hug and then asks, "How soon can we go?"

Grandpa Ben says, "We'll leave for your house in Naugatuck tomorrow morning and then catch an early morning train for Boston on Saturday. Now Phil, I received your parents' permission to take you, but only for the weekend. We'll be taking the train back on Sunday afternoon. Get a good night's sleep tonight because we'll be up tomorrow at the crack of dawn."

"Will we be taking your horse and buggy to Naugatuck?"

"That we will," says Grandpa Ben, who then bids his grandson goodnight and closes the door to Phil's room. Phil liked riding in the horse and buggy, but secretly he wished there was a faster way to get home. For now, he lies in bed in his room on the top floor of the farmhouse. Through his spyglass, he can see the stars out his bedroom window. He begins to count them, 1, 2, 3, ... 46 stars can be seen in the night sky. Phil thinks, "That's one for each of the 46 states." Then he notices a single golden star. He had seen this star before. Surely it was a sign of the future, but what did it mean? He wonders for a while, but is soon sound asleep.

Each morning, without fail, Phil awakes to the crow of the farm's giant rooster. On Friday morning, August 20, he doesn't hear that crow. Instead, he hears a noise that sounds like a horn. Phil's grandfather soon enters his room and says, "Rise and shine, Phil. Our ride has arrived."

"Ride?" asks Phil. "What ride?" Peeking out his window, Phil cannot believe his eyes. In front of the farmhouse is an automobile, a 1909 Model T Ford, all shined up and ready to transport them to Naugatuck. A minute later there is a knock at the door, and Grandpa Ben greets his guest. Phil dashes downstairs, and his grandfather makes the introduction.

"Phil, this is my neighbor, Bill Jones. Bill, this is my grandson, Phil."

Bill extends his hand and says, "Good morning, Phil. Are you ready for your first ride in an automobile?"

"Ready!" responds Phil. "Am I ever." He races out the front door to take a closer look. "It's beautiful, Mr. Jones," he exclaims. "When can we go?" Within 10 minutes, all three are seated in the Model T, with Phil in the back seat. Suddenly, Phil jumps out and runs back into the farmhouse. A moment later he is back, clutching his spyglass. He turns to his grandfather and says, "I almost forgot this, Grandpa!"

The trip to Naugatuck by horse and buggy would take the better part of a day. In the Model T, they will be there in half that time. Over the rutted dirt roads they travel at speeds between 10 and 15 miles per hour. Bill begins the conversation.

"It's nice to finally meet you, Phil. Your grandfather talks about you all the time. I don't recall him mentioning your age. How old are you?"

"I'm 14," says Phil.

"Ah, to be 14 years old again," responds Bill, as he winks at Grandpa Ben. "What would you like to do with your life, son?"

"I'm not sure I understand your question," says Phil.

"What I mean is, what type of job would you like to have in the future? What excites you? What interests you?"

"I like many things," says Phil. "I like fishing with my friends and working around my grandpa's farm. I like horses, I like to play football, and I like children."

"That's a good start," says Bill. "You could be a farmer like your grandpa or drive a horse-drawn wagon for a local business. You could be a schoolteacher, or maybe even President of the United States, like Mr. Roosevelt or Mr. Taft. You could be anything you set your mind to be, Phil. Just let your imagination take you there, set a goal for yourself, and never give up on it."

Phil grins and says, "I never thought of it that way, Mr. Jones. I guess if I use my imagination, set a goal, and work hard, I *can* do almost anything."

"Right you are, son!" says Bill. "What's that you have in your hand, Phil?"

"It's my spyglass. Grandpa gave it to me. He says it came from Boston and once belonged to his grandfather. I use it to look at things around the farm, and I wanted to be sure to take it to Boston so I can get a close-up view of the city."

"Sounds like a fine idea to me," says Bill.

By mid afternoon, the Model T reaches the Edwards home in the Millville section of Naugatuck. Phil's parents are there to greet them. Bill will stay for the evening and drive Grandpa Ben and Phil to the train station in the early morning. Phil's mother prepares a wonderful meal, which everyone enjoys. The weary travelers agree that food has never tasted so good.

After a good night's sleep, Phil, his grandpa, and Bill Jones are up at 6:30 a.m. on Saturday, August 21, to drive to Waterbury's Union Station. The train departs for Boston's South Station at 8:30 a.m. As the Model T nears Union Station, Grandpa Ben notices the railroad building's impressive brick tower. The tower stands 240 feet high, and its face features a clock with a 16 ft. dial. It is the largest tower clock in New England and one of the largest in the United States. Phil notices that the time is just past 8 a.m.

Bill parks the Model T just outside the station, and Grandpa Ben and Phil take their one small suitcase from the automobile. They thank Bill for all his help, and soon he is on his way back home. Phil and his grandpa enter the station and step into the impressive waiting room. Just last month, on July 11, Union Station had opened to the public, and everything about it is new, fresh, and clean. From the high ceiling hang three large cast-iron chandeliers. Three large windows are positioned on each side of the waiting room. The tile floor is covered with high-backed waiting chairs.

Grandpa Ben and Phil walk to the ticket office, which is just opposite the main entrance. Before them are three ticket windows with fancy brass fronts and marble cash counters. Here, Grandpa Ben purchases two tickets to Boston. The time is now 8:20 a.m. Soon, the cry of "all aboard for Hartford and Boston" is heard, and the two excited passengers board the train.

Phil and his grandfather take their seats inside the passenger car. As the steam train pulls out of the station, its whistle blows as if to announce the start of their adventure. From the window near his seat, Phil soon watches the landscape speed by at 40 miles per hour.

"I'm so excited, Grandpa. I can't wait to get there," he says. "Can you tell me some of the family stories again? Maybe it will make the time go by faster."

"Sure I can, Phil. You'll recall I never have a problem telling a good story. I know I've told you about the sea captain and my grandfather Ben the cooper, and his Uncle Alex and the Sons of Liberty. Perhaps I can tell you more about some of the other family members. Ben's sister, Sally, married Paul Revere Jr., as you know, and they had quite a few children—I believe at least 10. Ben's cousin, Betsey, married Jedediah Lincoln. He was descended from Samuel Lincoln of Hingham, Massachusetts, a small town 10 miles south of Boston. President Abraham Lincoln was also descended from Samuel Lincoln.

"When Betsey died in 1796, Jedediah Lincoln remarried to Mary Revere, daughter of Paul Revere. His brother, Amos Lincoln, who participated in the Boston Tea Party, also married one of Paul Revere's daughters, Deborah, and later, her sister, Elizabeth."

Since the topic at hand was the Lincoln family, Phil took the opportunity to impress his grandfather.

"Grandpa, I tried to memorize President Lincoln's speech that you showed me recently. Would you like to hear it?"

"The Gettysburg Address?"

"Yes, Grandpa. We'll be studying the Civil War in school come September. I'll be in the 7th grade, and I thought it would be good to learn it."

"Let's hear what you've memorized."

"Four score and seven years ago our fathers brought forth on this continent, a new nation, conceived in Liberty, and dedicated to the proposition that all men are created equal ..."

Phil is able to get part way through the speech before forgetting what comes next. Grandpa Ben is pleased with the effort. He writes down the lines that Phil has missed and then replies, "It's impressive to memorize such a speech, but even more important to understand its meaning. Do you understand what President Lincoln is talking about?"

"I'm not really sure," answers Phil.

"At a time of crisis, Lincoln is recalling the ideals that this nation was founded upon. The Founding Fathers established these ideals and wrote them in the Declaration of Independence: the belief in human equality; the belief that this experiment in self-government called the United States of America could succeed. 'The brave men, living and dead, who struggled here,' as Lincoln described them, fought for that belief.

"Today, Phil, we are traveling to Boston to see where the road to freedom began. The 'new birth of freedom' that President Lincoln predicted in the Gettysburg Address would not be possible without the sacrifice of many, including the men he honored that day."

Grandpa Ben hands Phil a piece of paper containing the lines he had forgotten.

"Now you can memorize it and understand it, too!"

Phil wasn't able to follow his grandfather's explanation completely, but it certainly did make him think.

"Thank you, Grandpa," he replied.

As the train pulls into South Station, the time is nearing 1 p.m. The station itself was completed at the turn of the century and, at that time, was the world's largest. Grandpa Ben and Phil leave the train and walk out the front entrance of the station. They find themselves on the corner of Summer Street and Atlantic Avenue, an area known to Bostonians as Dewey Square.

Grandpa Ben grew up in Boston, and, although many years have passed, he still has a good sense for which direction they should travel in.

The day is cloudy, and it looks as if it might rain.

"I wish the weather were a bit brighter," says Grandpa Ben.

"It will be," says Phil. "The sun will be out soon, Grandpa. I'm certain of it."

Grandpa Ben laughs, recalling the many times that his grandson's predictions have come true.

Phil peers at the buildings in the city through his spyglass. He is amazed by what he sees. He and his grandpa walk down Summer Street and then Winter Street until they reach the intersection with Tremont Street. Here, Grandpa Ben sees something that certainly wasn't here when he was a boy. It wasn't built until 1897. Before them, on the corner of Park and Tremont streets, is the Park Street Subway Station.

"Grandpa, what's this?" asks Phil.

"It's the subway, Phil. It's an underground train that goes to other parts of the city."

"A train—underground! Can we go on it, please Grandpa, can we?"

Grandpa Ben asks the man at the ticket booth if the subway will take them toward the North End. The answer is "Yes." He then purchases two tickets, follows his grandson down a flight of stairs, and their adventure continues. Phil loves the subway ride. "I can't wait to tell my parents that I rode on a train underground!" he says. The subway train travels a short distance and takes them to North Station. When the travelers exit the train and continue their journey, they find themselves on Causeway Street. Here Grandpa Ben and Phil walk north toward Commercial Street and eventually take a right on Hull Street.

To their left is the entrance to Copp's Hill Burying Ground. Grandpa Ben shows his grandson the slate marker that reads "Capt. Benjamin Edwards Tomb."

"This is the family tomb. The sea captain is here, and so is Uncle Alex, Ben the cooper, his sister Sally, and his cousin Betsey. Members of the Revere and Lincoln families who are related to the Edwards family through marriage also rest here. They include Paul Revere Jr. and Jedediah Lincoln."

For the first time, Phil is seeing proof that his grandfather's stories are true. Grandpa Ben reaches into his pocket and pulls out a small scrap of wood. He places the piece of wood on top of the marker. "Now that's something I haven't done since my father took me here when I was a child," he says.

"Why did you put that piece of wood on top of the marker, Grandpa?" asks Phil.

"It's a family tradition," he says, "a way to leave proof of our visit."

Phil finds a twig nearby and places it next to Grandpa Ben's item on top of the slate marker. "I want my ancestors to know that I was here, too," he says.

Grandpa Ben smiles and then adds, "Follow me." They walk to the other end of the burying ground to view a marker leaning up against the wall. "This is the marker of Robert Newman. I've mentioned his name to you before. Paul Revere asked Robert Newman and John Pulling to hold two lanterns in a window of the Old North Church steeple to warn the Sons of Liberty in Charlestown. John Pulling is also buried here."

"Is there really an Old North Church, Grandpa?"

"There certainly is," he replies.

As they leave the burying ground, Grandpa Ben points down Hull Street and says, "Here it is." Phil views the steeple through his spyglass. Below the steeple there is a plaque. Grandpa Ben reads the words on this plaque out loud.

"The signal lanterns of Paul Revere displayed in the steeple of this church April 18, 1775 warned the country of the march of the British troops to Lexington and Concord."

"Grandpa, can we go inside?"

"I believe we can, Phil. Let's walk down and take a look."

Phil is too excited to "walk," so he runs as fast as he can down the paved stone street that leads to the church. Finding the door open, he steps inside. Phil notices the high box pews and the two brass chandeliers that hang above the central aisle. He counts 12 candles on each of them. Soon his grandfather joins him.

"When my grandfather lived in Boston, they called this wonderful building Christ Church. Today, most folks call it the Old North Church."

"Can we climb into the steeple, Grandpa?"

"I don't believe we have time for that, Phil. We have so many other places to visit. Didn't you say you wanted to see where Paul Revere lived?"

"I would like that," says Phil. "Maybe tomorrow we can climb the steeple."

They walk a few blocks to North Square where the Revere home is located. It had recently been restored and was opened to the public on April 18, 1908. As they reach the home, Grandpa Ben starts to laugh.

"What's so funny Grandpa?" asks Phil.

"It seems you're right again, Phil. About the weather that is."

The sky has begun to clear, and an area of sunlight can be seen just ahead of them.

"I saw that yesterday through the spyglass you gave me. I'm seeing more things through it each day, I'm just not sure what they all mean."

Grandpa Ben knocks at the front door of the Revere home, and a gentleman soon opens it. He takes their admission and invites them in. They walk into the living room, where they see a gateleg table, a Colonial highboy dresser, and portraits of Paul and Rachel Revere. Fancy wallpaper covers the walls. Beyond the living room, in the kitchen, they view a fireplace, with tools for cooking, a spinning wheel and a cradle for a small child. They walk upstairs and enter Paul Revere's bedchamber.

Phil asks his grandfather a question: "Grandpa, is that Paul Revere's real bed, is that the way he left it?"

Grandpa Ben chuckles and then responds, "I don't know the answer to that, Phil. Perhaps we'll meet someone who does."

"Did he leave from here for his Midnight Ride?"

A woman standing in the background overhears them and answers the question before Phil's grandfather can.

"Yes he did. He left from the front door of this very home on the evening of April 18, 1775. I'm pleased to see that the younger generation has such an interest in American history. When I see that interest, it makes me happy that we restored this home. Let me introduce myself. My name is Pauline Revere Thayer."

Grandpa Ben and Phil introduce themselves.

"My father, Paul Joseph Revere, was Paul Revere's grandson. He was a patriot very much like his grandfather. He fought in the Civil War," says Pauline.

"In the Civil War!" says Phil.

"Yes, he was a member of the 20th Massachusetts Volunteer Infantry. He fought at Gettysburg."

"Gettysburg!!" exclaims Phil.

"My, you do have an interest in American history. Wait for just a moment, there's something I'd like to show you." Pauline soon returns, holding a book in her right hand. The green cover is imprinted in gold with the words "Revere Memorial." Pauline opens the book to page 182 and prepares to read a passage.

"My father wrote this letter to my mother in 1863, when I was 16 months old."

Thursday, July 2.

We marched yesterday to near Gettysburg; and, this morning, moved to the rear of the town. There seems a prospect of an engagement. In case one should occur, we all hope it may be a general one, as, from the position of the armies, it seems it must prove decisive. For myself, I feel that God will order what is best for us all. May he bless you and our dear children and all at home! I received Josie's letter yesterday with our dear little heart's photograph. He looks quite like a man, and old enough to take care of his mamma. Tell him I say so, and shall depend on his doing so.

P.J.R.

"I would like to meet your father someday," says Phil. "I am very interested in the Civil War. May I write to him?"

"My father, Colonel Paul Joseph Revere, was badly wounded at Gettysburg the same day he wrote the letter I have just read. He died two days later, on July 4th, moments after hearing the news of the Union victory. His brother, Edward, had died 10 months earlier at the Battle of Antietam."

"I'm really sorry," says Phil, bowing his head. Before Pauline closes the book, she shows Phil the first page, which reads, "A Memorial of Paul Joseph Revere and Edward H. R. Revere." The book was printed in Boston in 1874.

Phil thinks for a moment and then asks Pauline an unusual question.

"Mrs. Thayer, did your father have a spyglass?"

Pauline looks surprised. "It's interesting that you should ask that, Phil," she says. "My father did carry a pair of field glasses (binoculars) with him during the war. Perhaps that is what you are referring to. He used them at Gettysburg. After his death, they were given to Lieutenant Colonel Peirson of the 39th Massachusetts. He was wearing them in a battle near Laurel Hill, Virginia, in 1864 when he was hit by an artillery shell fragment. The field glasses were badly damaged when he was struck. The Lieutenant Colonel always felt those field glasses saved his life."

Grandpa Ben continues the conversation with Pauline, mentioning the family's relation to Sally Edwards, who married Paul Revere Jr., and telling other tales of his Boston ancestors. When they bid goodbye, Pauline thanks Grandpa Ben and Phil for visiting and adds, "Please come again soon."

After Phil and his grandfather leave, they eat supper and then find a hotel room for the evening. On Sunday, August 22, they walk through the market at Faneuil Hall and view the balcony of the Old State House before taking the train back to Waterbury. On the train, Phil thinks of his conversation with Pauline Revere Thayer. Her father was one of the "brave men" that President Lincoln wrote about in his address. Phil is deep in thought when his grandfather interrupts him.

"How's that speech coming along, Phil?"

Phil, once again, tries to deliver President Lincoln's address. This time he gets further than his first attempt. His grand-father says, "Well done, Phil. That type of progress deserves some kind of reward." Reaching into his pocket, he pulls out a handful of change. Among the Indian Head cents, there is a new penny with a picture of Abraham Lincoln on it. It was just introduced this year in celebration of the Lincoln Centennial (the 100th anniversary of Abraham Lincoln's birth). He gives Phil the 1909 Lincoln cent and says, "Keep up the good work."

Phil admires the shiny new coin. It is the first to contain the image of a U.S. president. Over Lincoln's head, Phil notices the words "In God We Trust" and to Lincoln's left, he spots the word "Liberty." Phil says, "Thank you, Grandpa, and thanks for taking me to Boston, too. Your stories that I've listened to for so many years mean more to me now than ever!"

As the train chugs along and the weekend adventure comes to a close, Grandpa Ben turns to his grandson and says, "Now that you know the people and places in my stories are real, there's something special I have to show you."

"What is it?" asks Phil.

"I'll bring it with me the next time I visit you. I keep it in a closet back at the farmhouse."

"I can't wait for your next visit."

As the train heads back to Waterbury, Grandpa Ben, the storyteller, says, "Have I ever told you this one, Phil ...?"

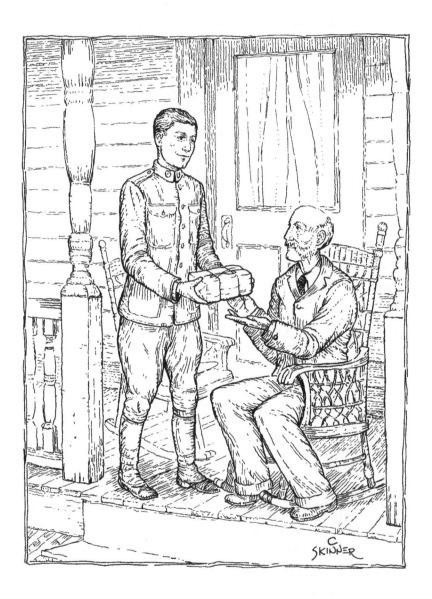

The Promise

A month after their trip to Boston, Grandpa Ben drives his horse and buggy to Naugatuck to see his grandson. He remembers to bring that "something special" he had mentioned in their last conversation. It is his father's family Bible, printed in 1812. He had never shown it to Phil before. Grandpa opens the Bible to the family record section. As they read the entries made there, Phil notices that a small card marks the location. The card reads "Happy New Year 1865."

"I put that card in this Bible when I was 29," says Grandpa Ben. "It had special meaning to me then and still does today."

Phil can feel a story coming on. Interested in the meaning behind the card, he says, "Grandpa, why did you save it?"

"I was told that my grandfather, Ben the cooper, was baptized in Boston on April 14, 1765. Realizing that the year 1865 was the 100th anniversary of his birth, I decided to save the card. When April 14, 1865 came, I can recall holding this card and thinking of my grandfather. That same evening, on Good Friday, in Washington, D.C., President Lincoln was shot. He died the next day. Years later, I read a book about him that said he had a particular dream over and over again. It related to water. In the dream, Lincoln was on a vessel at sea 'moving with great rapidity toward a dark and indefinite shore,' as he described it. The dream always happened before a big event, usually a Union victory. The last time Lincoln had the dream, he reported it at a cabinet meeting the next day. That was April 14, 1865.

"When I read that book, I remember thinking 'in a way, Lincoln dreamed of being a mariner just like Ben the cooper did.' That's why I saved this card for all those years."

Phil had a special appreciation for Ben the cooper because, as he had learned from his grandfather, Ben had had a dream and a goal and had never given up on them. Phil had dreams and goals for his life, too, and like his ancestor, he was determined that nothing would stand in his way.

Phil put his goals in writing and reviewed them each day. As the years passed, he understood the path his life would take. Phil was admired by everyone he met, especially the neighborhood children. In 1915, he drove a horse-drawn wagon and delivered groceries for the local market in Millville. The children would wait for Phil along his route. They knew he would stop for them.

One at a time, Phil picked them up and sat them beside him. As they traveled to the next house, he told them stories and was sure to ask, "What would you like to do with your life?" Once he heard their answers, he would always add, "That's a good start. Remember, you can be anything you set your mind to be. Just set a goal for yourself and never give up on it." Phil loved these children dearly.

Phil had finally memorized President Lincoln's speech and would recite it to the children and challenge them to repeat it back. After they tried, he was sure to say, "It's impressive to memorize such a speech, but even more important to understand its meaning." Phil believed he understood that meaning. At the end of his route each day, he'd stop the wagon in front of the market, just beneath an American flag. He would sit alone for a moment and count the stars, 1, 2, 3, ... 48 stars for the 48 United States. He was so proud of that flag.

Phil's favorite stop on his route was the Wininger home. Here, he'd visit his sweetheart, 15-year-old Ella Wininger and her little sister Doris. Over the years, Ella's love for pond lilies remained, and her feelings for Phil grew. Phil was Ella's "first love," and he felt that she was "the only girl for him." They spoke of plans to marry in a few years and both wanted a large family. Ella certainly shared Phil's love for children. They would live on a farm, own a few horses, and grow old together. Everyone said they made the perfect couple.

In April of 1917, the United States entered World War I, and Phil and Ella were forced to put their plans for the future on hold. Phil and his best friend, John Simmons, enlisted shortly after the U.S. declared war on Germany. On April 14, 1917, they joined the Connecticut National Guard. Their pal, Warren Birdsall, soon enlisted. During the next few months, all three trained at Yale field in New Haven.

It appeared they would be going to France soon. Phil, John, and Warren took two-day passes to spend time with their families before they headed "over there." Phil spent the first day of his leave with Ella. On a sunny afternoon, they walked through the apple orchard next to the Elliott farm. It was one of their favorite spots. Phil and Ella sat beneath a familiar tree and began to talk.

"Underneath this tree, we kissed for the first time. Do you remember that day?" asked Ella.

"I'll never forget it," said Phil. "I remember how you and Ethel would sneak into the orchard to meet with John and me when her Pa thought both of you were doing chores. John always laughed about those secret meetings."

"I'm sure Ethel's father caught on, but he never stopped us," said Ella. "Maybe he remembered what it was like to be young and in love."

"Maybe," said Phil.

Ella smiled and then grew quiet. "I'm afraid, Phil," she said.

"Afraid of what?" he asked.

"Afraid you might never return from France. I don't know what I'd do without you. Please tell me you'll come back. Then we can get married and have lots of kids so you'll have someone to pass on that spyglass of yours to. Isn't that how your family tradition works?"

"The spyglass has been passed down in the family since the American Revolution, and it's my job to pass it on to the next generation," said Phil.

"So you'll pass it on to our children, and they'll pass it on to theirs," said Ella.

"Ben the cooper got the spyglass from his Uncle Alex when he was a boy in Boston," said Phil. "Uncle Alex and Aunt Sarah never had any children of their own. They raised Ben and eight other orphans. What I'm trying to say is the spyglass is not only for our children, Ella, but for every child who believes in it. I want to pass it on to as many of them as I can."

"I'm not sure I understand, Phil," said Ella.

"In time you will," said Phil. "For now, I've got a little surprise. Close your eyes and don't peek."

Ella giggled. "What are you up to, Phil?"

Phil reached into his pocket and pulled out a chain with a beautiful gold locket attached. "Open your eyes," he said.

For a moment, Ella was speechless. Finally, she said, "It's the most beautiful thing I've ever seen."

Phil put the locket around her neck and said, "I wanted to give you something before I left so you'd know how much I love you. No matter what happens, we'll always be together. Always."

Ella gave Phil a kiss, and he wiped the tears from her eyes.

Don't be afraid," he said. "Now that the Yanks have joined the fight, the war will soon be over."

Ella believed what Phil was telling her, but it didn't make his leaving any easier. "Philip Edwards," she said, "say you'll write to me as often as you can. Just hearing from you will make me feel better."

"I'll write every chance I get," said Phil, as they both stood up and began to walk back toward the Wininger home. As Phil and Ella strode across the small wooden bridge that spanned Long Meadow Brook, Phil said, "I'm going to miss this town. I don't know what to expect when we get to France. Boston is about the farthest I've ever been from home. It sure will be an adventure though, Ella. I mean, being on a ship and all. Maybe this is how Ben the cooper felt."

Phil walked Ella to the front door of her home, and her seven-year-old sister Doris met them there. She often hid when Phil visited Ella, but not today.

"I wanted to say hello," said Doris. "Ella told me you would be going away. I'll miss you, Phil."

Phil picked Doris up and gave her a hug. "I'll miss you, too," he said.

"How long will you be gone?" asked Doris.

Phil thought for a moment and then said, "I don't know."

Doris crossed her arms and stared into Phil's eyes. "I just want to remember your face," she said. "I'll keep a picture of you in my head until you come home."

Ella smiled.

The front door opened, and John Wininger and his wife Daisy appeared. They both greeted Phil. John shook his hand and said a few words.

"I wish you were going on a fishing trip, like in the old days. Instead, you're off to fight. When do you expect to ship out?"

"They're not saying sir, but I feel it will be soon."

"God go with you," said John.

Ella's mom hugged Phil and said, "Be careful and come home to us."

"I'll do that," replied Phil.

When the conversation ended, the Wininger's took Doris inside and left Phil and Ella alone. The young couple kissed, shed a few tears, and said goodbye.

As Phil walked toward home, two familiar voices called out his name. He spotted his best friend, John Simmons, and Ethel Elliott approaching. Phil and Ella were not the only sweethearts from Millville. John and Ethel had been courting as well. They had taken a walk into town and were returning to the Elliott farm. They knew that Phil was giving Ella the locket and were anxious to know what had happened. Phil told them how much Ella had loved it and how he had given it to her in the orchard, just as he had planned. When they said goodbye, Phil told John he would see him at his home the next day.

Phil spent the last day of his leave at the family home in Naugatuck, talking with his parents, Ben and Minnie. They were both so proud of him. Phil was dressed in his National Guard uniform. He would report back for duty that afternoon. His mother kept a picture of Phil in uniform on a mahogany table in the dining room. As their conversation drew to a close, Phil hugged his parents and told them he'd write. They all said a prayer together, and when they were done, Phil walked upstairs, retrieved an item from his room, and went outside on the porch.

Grandpa Ben was seated in his favorite rocking chair on the front porch. In the summer of 1917, he was 81 years old but still in excellent health. Phil approached his grandfather and began to speak.

"Grandpa, I want to thank you for everything you've given me. I'll always remember your stories and the trip we took to Boston and what I learned there. Soon I'll be going to France to fight in the war. I pray this will be the war to end all wars, one that makes the world safe for democracy. I have so much to live for, Grandpa, so many goals and so many dreams. But the love I feel for my country is greater than all of them combined. It's important that you know I feel this way."

Phil then handed his grandfather a package he was holding behind his back. The box was wrapped in brown paper and tied with string.

Grandpa Ben looked confused. "What's this?" he asked his grandson.

"Hold on to it, Grandpa, and don't open it until I return. Promise me, Grandpa."

Grandpa Ben agreed, and Phil gave him a big hug and said goodbye.

Phil began the walk to John Simmons' home on Carroll Street. Phil and John would be returning for duty together, along with their pal, Warren Birdsall. On the way to John's home, Phil was surprised when six of the neighborhood children raced up to see him. Ella had passed the word that he was in town, and they had hoped to visit with him before he left.

It had been a while since Phil made deliveries by horse-drawn wagon and took them for rides, but these children were always on his mind. They never forgot Phil, either. They remembered his stories and the question he would always ask, "What would you like to do with your life?" As they walked beside him, each of them described their latest answer to that question. Phil was pleased with those answers, and before he said goodbye, he encouraged each of them to reach for their dreams.

In August of 1917, the 26th or "Yankee" Division of the American Expeditionary Force was formed in Boston. The Connecticut National Guard soon joined the 26th. They became part of its 102nd Infantry Regiment. Phil and John were members of Company H of the 102nd, and Warren was in Company B.

Phil, John, Warren, and other members of the 102nd left for Liverpool, England, aboard the British liner *Adriatic* on October 27. Phil sensed that this was the English ship he had seen through his spyglass. They arrived on November 10 and were transported across the English Channel to France a few days later. They arrived at training camp in the small town of Rouvres-la-Chétive on November 14 and trained there for three months. The weather was cold and rainy, and mud was everywhere. The weather improved for a time in early February of 1918, and on the 5th, they left for the trenches. As he had promised, Phil wrote letters to Ella and his parents as often as he could.

One of his letters, written on July 10, arrived at the family home in early August. In the last paragraph, he mentioned, "we are still at the front." A censor had crossed out "the front" in pencil, but the words were still visible. Ella received a letter around the same time. It was dated July 12. In it, Phil made a unique reference to being in the front line trenches when he told Ella, "I have seen all the side shows, and am now at the circus."

On Monday, August 12, 1918, the Edwards family received a telegram from the War Department notifying them that their son Phil had been killed in action in France on July 9. His parents hoped there had been a mistake. Phil could not have been killed on July 9. He had sent letters home dated July 10 and 12. Ben and Minnie Edwards responded to the War Department by telegram, asking for verification. For five days, there was no reply. On Sunday, August 18, the following letter arrived at the Edwards home:

July 19, 1918

My Dear Mother and Father,

We have started a big allied drive and our regiment is "going over the top" in a short while. I am writing a short farewell message, which will be mailed to you if I am killed, and if not, you will never see it.

I have read my Bible, and said my prayers. I believe all my sins are forgiven and I do not fear death in the least. I know that it will be heart-breaking news for you to receive this letter. But remember, we are fighting for a good cause and I think that this drive will bring peace. Tell all the boys and girls that I died game and I honestly hope none of them will ever have to get into war.

God bless and keep you both.

Your loving son to the last,

Phil

Phil was killed in action on July 21, 1918, near Château-Thierry, France. He was 23 years old. Just like the brave patriots in his grandfather's stories, and many that would follow him, Phil gave up his life so that many of us would have the opportunity to live ours in freedom.

Phil's mother Minnie kept a service flag in the window of her Millville home. Its deep blue star indicated that the family had a member in the service. After her son's farewell letter arrived, the deep blue star was soon covered with a gold star, the sign to all that a member of the family had made the supreme sacrifice for his country.

After hearing the news of Phil's death, Grandpa Ben was so sad that he didn't leave his room for days. Then, he remembered the package that Phil had given him. Grandpa Ben had kept it beneath his bed. He also remembered Phil's instructions "Don't open it until I return." He intended to keep that promise.

In early September, a letter arrived from John Simmons. John had been like a second son to Minnie and Ben Edwards. He wanted to express his feelings about the loss of their son, his closest friend:

France, Aug. 3, 1918

Dear Mother and Dad,

This is about the hardest letter I ever had to write and I don't know how to begin. I guess you have heard the sad news by now and I know what a shock it must have been to you. I wasn't with Phil when it happened as I was in a different part of the field and I didn't hear about it until that night. One of the runners told me then and I couldn't believe it at first. You can guess what a shock it gave me and I miss him more than I can say. Even now it doesn't seem real and I can't hardly believe that dear old Phil has gone for good. He was always a fine, brave lad and he was killed while doing his duty. I know he didn't suffer much for he was killed instantly and there was only one little mark on him. He was hit by a small piece of shell, but I think it was the concussion which killed him.

I would have written sooner, but I haven't had much chance as we have been constantly on the move and paper was hard to get. You probably have heard about the battle which is still going on and the Yankee boys are certainly giving Fritz something to think about and I guess before he's through with us he will see that in tackling the despised recruits from over the sea, he has bitten off more than he can chew. I can't think about more to write now and I pray the Lord will give you strength to bear your sorrow. I wish that I could lighten it for you and I wish that it was I instead of Phil that had to go. Will close now, with love.

From John
P.S. Warren was all right the last time I saw him and he felt pretty blue.

The war ended in November of 1918. The 26th Division began leaving France on March 20, 1919, and the first troop ship arrived in Boston on April 4. An impressive "Welcome Home" parade to honor the brave boys of the 26th Division took place in Boston on April 25, 1919. The troops gathered for the parade on the corner of Beacon and Charles streets by Boston Common. Large crowds of cheering Bostonians lined the route, which made its way through the streets of Back Bay.

A police escort was followed by Major General Clarence Edwards and his staff and the 26th Division Flag of Honor. Behind the flag was a 220-millimeter howitzer captured by the 26th Division on the day Phil was killed, July 21, 1918. Wounded soldiers of the 26th followed in automobiles, and then each regiment and battalion appeared. Marching sixth in line were the members of Phil's regiment, the 102nd Infantry. If only in spirit, Phil was surely with them on this day.

Phil rested in an American cemetery located beside a lonely country road near the small French town of Epieds. His grave was marked by a simple wooden cross that contained the name "Philip Edwards." It was surrounded by hundreds of similar crosses that marked the graves of American soldiers. Phil's parents wanted their son's body returned to the United States. He was their only child and their hero. It took nearly three years, but their efforts were finally successful.

On his final journey, Phil traveled from France to the port of Antwerp, Belgium where his body was placed aboard the U.S. Army transport ship *Wheaton*. After a 23-day ocean voyage, the *Wheaton* reached Hoboken, New Jersey on July 2, 1921. Phil's body left New York on July 15 aboard a New York, New Haven and Hartford Railroad train with Private

John McCarthy of the 16th Infantry serving as his military escort. Later that day, Phil was home.

On July 17, 1921, Philip Edwards received one of the most impressive military funerals ever held in Naugatuck. The eulogy at the Congregational Church was made more stirring when Reverend Edward R. Hance read Phil's farewell letter. Ella Wininger knelt beside his flag-draped casket and placed a single rose on top of it. It was her way of welcoming her soldier home and saying goodbye.

John Simmons, Warren Birdsall, and Phil's other buddies from the 102nd Regiment were there in uniform to pay tribute to their friend. As he was laid to rest at Grove Cemetery, they held a flag that contained 48 stars in a field of blue, surrounded by 13 alternating red and white stripes. They folded that flag with great precision and handed it to Phil's mother. A salute was fired. Taps was sounded.

As Phil's casket was lowered, John Simmons and his wife, Ethel Elliott, consoled Ella, Phil's parents, and his many relatives. The next day, when Phil's grandfather returned home, he reached beneath his bed and located the package that Phil had given him. Slowly, he untied the string and then removed the brown wrapping paper. Finally, he opened the box. It contained Phil's spyglass and a rolled up piece of paper. Grandpa Ben unrolled the paper and began to read it.

Dear Grandpa,

Thank you for giving this to me. I did my best to pass it on to the neighborhood children. I believe that each of them has it now. Tell them I said so, and that they should remember, "if they use it, they can be anything they set their minds to be, as long as they set a goal for themselves and NEVER give up on it."

God bless and keep you.
Your grandson,
Phil

P.S. Please tell Ella not to be sad, for we WILL meet again. Until then, I'll be beside her, watching over her every day.

Grandpa Ben delivered Phil's message to Ella and the neighborhood children. Each Memorial Day there was a parade in Naugatuck, and Ella and the children never missed it. They waved their American flags and remembered Phil and all that he stood for. Soon, the flag that Phil loved had 50 stars. Those children followed Phil's advice, and, with Ella's guidance, they created goals for themselves, worked hard, and each of them became exactly what they wanted to be.

Ella became a nurse in 1921, and she spent her life caring for others. At the age of 21, she married Myron Boardman. They lived happily on a farm in Granby, Connecticut, and owned several horses. Ella never had any children of her own, but she touched the lives of so many children and they all loved her. Ella always wore the locket that Phil gave her, and she visited his marker at Grove Cemetery often. Ella died in 1992 at the age of 92.

Today, the children from the neighborhood, some well into their 90s, still speak fondly of Ella and Phil. Their love was endless—a timeless wonder—just like the rides Phil gave so long ago, in the horse-drawn wagon. They can still recall the stories Phil told—stories about the future. They say he had quite an imagination ....

— The End —

Did the Spyglass Really Exist?

The answer to that question is "Yes," if you believe in the power of a child's imagination. In *One April in Boston*, young Ben had a wonderful gift. He had the ability to picture his future and to take steps toward achieving what he saw. He set a goal for himself, wrote it down, and reviewed it every day. This alone, he learned, was not enough. He heard this message from a man named John Pulling, as they both shared a view from atop the highest steeple in all of Boston. John taught Ben that he must do something each day to help him reach his goal.

Although his sister Sally and cousin Rebecca teased him about his plans, Ben found allies in his cousin Betsey and his Uncle Alex. Betsey believed in the power of Ben's imagination and supported him, while Uncle Alex provided him with the tools and training he would need to reach his goal. Ben realized the value of these two relationships and made every effort to help his cousin and learn from his uncle.

Ben was blessed with both an active imagination and an ability to glimpse future events. In the story, some of Ben's visions started to come true. When this happened, Ben gained confidence in his visions for his own future. Even after Ben reached his goal of working on a sailing ship, he continued to carry the spyglass with him, using his imagination to create a brighter future for himself.

The gift that young Ben had was passed on to his son, Joseph, and then to Joseph's son, Benjamin. A 70-year-old Benjamin passed the gift of the spyglass on to his young grandson, Phil. In the story, Phil learned that "he can be anything he sets his mind to be as long as he sets a goal for himself and never gives up on it." The trip he took to Boston brought his grandpa's stories to life, and Phil gained a real appreciation for American history and the sacrifices made by patriotic Americans. As time passed, and Phil glimpsed more of the future, he "understood the path his life would take."

Phil's love for his country was equaled only by his love for Ella and the neighborhood children. He wanted to pass the gift of the spyglass on to those children while he still had time. He left, not knowing for sure, but hoping that he had reached that goal. He returned as a hero to a hometown that honored his memory.

The children that Phil loved used the gift he gave them and "became exactly what they wanted to be." Through this book, that same gift is passed on to you, the reader. Believe in the spyglass and believe that it is within your grasp. Use the power of your imagination to set goals for yourself, write them down, take action toward their achievement each day, and NEVER give up on them. Dream big dreams, and you too "can be anything you set your mind to be."

New Illustrations for the Second Edition

Illustrator Cortney Skinner created 26 new illustrations for the second edition of *One April in Boston* and 19 of those are featured in this section. Below is a bit of his personal insight into each of those illustrations. Reading this will give you a better appreciation for and understanding of the illustrations themselves.

1) The Edwards family home

Using the original photo, circa 1905, as a reference, I saw that the Edwards family home was a very plain and simple, front-gabled mid-19th century house, the only ornamentation being the brackets at the top of the porch supports. Little 10-year-old Phil and his grandma in the rattan chair relax on the porch. Someone in the family has set out a flower box at the corner of the porch. Behind the house can just be glimpsed what may be a carriage house. In the reference photo, I could see what looked like a vegetable garden to the left of the house. A house is a reflection of its occupants, and this one looks very strong, honest, and uncomplicated.

2) The original photo, circa 1905, of the Edwards family home in the Millville section of Naugatuck, Connecticut that Cortney used as a reference for his illustration

3) The Edwards family on the front porch

While doing the very detailed drawing and studying the postures, attitudes and "body English" of this family as I interpreted it in pen and ink, I was noticing some very interesting things. This sort of close observation is something I regularly do as an artist when drawing or painting people.

I was noticing what a close-knit family they had to have been, given all the little visual clues in the original photo.

This is especially interesting considering the period in which this photograph was taken, which is one popularly considered to be stiff and formal. My guess is that this was not taken with a small hand-held camera, but with a larger, formal, and professional camera on a tripod—probably a large view camera and taken at the same time that the house photograph was taken, since it looks like Phil is wearing the same shirt in both photos, and the season is the same.

The father and son are seated closely together, the son not at all bashful about resting his hand on his father's hand, and curling/bending his left leg inward as if to get even closer to his father. This detail was lost in the darkness of the photo until I lightened the exposure to give me more information for doing the drawing. Little Phil is also leaning into his father's chest, and the mother is also leaning, inclined towards both of them. Even the young lady is inclined toward the group. Grandma in the wicker chair is relaxed, sitting back, and with a hint of a smile on her lips. She's not at all sitting stiffly or formally.

There's not much open space at all between these family members. This is a close and relaxed family.

4) The original photo, circa 1905, of the Edwards family on the front porch that Cortney used as a reference for his illustration

5) Phil in his room

For this drawing of young Phil in his room, I had to imagine how his room might have been furnished. Given the simplicity and straightforwardness of his house's exterior, I imagined Phil's room was likewise simply furnished with a mid-century oak table, and a simple wood bed with a quilt handed down through generations of the Edwards family. These were the days when indoor plumbing was not as present throughout the house as today, so there's a washbasin and pitcher on the table next to Phil's spyglass and a couple glass marbles. Phil reads his American history book, and a framed photo of Abraham Lincoln hangs next to pictures of 18th century sailing ships torn from magazines and thumbtacked on the wall by Phil, reminders of his ancestors' sailing past.

6) Phil sees the *Adriatic* through his spyglass

This scene is more of a lyrical one rather than a factual one. Though the ship Phil left for France aboard was heavily researched and authentically portrayed, its outsize British flag (rather than the smaller white ensign of the Royal Navy) was used for its symbolism and instant recognizability. Phil stands on a hill near his home and what he sees in his spyglass we see symbolically suspended in the clouds.

7) Phil gives Ella the pond lilies

This illustration was interesting to undertake. Not only were the clothes exhaustively researched (correct period bib overalls, hats, dresses, and shoes) but also examples of early fishing rods and gear needed to be found so that I could represent the period correctly. Naturally, the pond lily had to be researched as well, but most interesting for me was regressing the ages of Phil, Ella, John, and Warren using photos of them at older ages. There's an entire forensic science created that has noted the changes in the human face owing to various ages … which is something that comes as a matter of course for illustrators who study human anatomy.

8) Phil, John, and Warren

This drawing was done using the original photo as a reference. It was an opportunity for me to study Phil's facial features at an age between his young boyhood and adulthood. Phil has a very strong nose and a dimple in his chin. Judging from the photo of his family when Phil was a young boy, these features were inherited from his father. I began to feel as if I knew Phil to some extent, after studying his photos and drawing him so many times.

9) The original photo, circa 1908, of Phil, John, and (probably) Warren that Cortney used as a reference for his illustration

10) Phil at the end of his route looking at the American flag

My usual historic research for this drawing included investigating the right sort of utility wagon for the period, and the correct way for Phil to hold the reins. That cast iron, horse head hitching post was borrowed from my own childhood. My neighborhood consisted of many Victorian houses and older streets with hitching posts just like this one.

11) Phil giving Ella the locket

It's always a challenge to draw real people in a scene that I could only imagine—especially if it's a scene of emotional significance. Body language, the expressions in the eyes and features, and even the symmetry of this drawing help to focus attention on the young couple's feelings. There is even an "Eden" symbolism in the apple trees in the background.

12) Phil, Ella, and Doris on the front porch of the Wininger home

This drawing is one of my personal favorites. Using a photograph of her head and shoulders at about this age, I drew Doris standing in a pose typical for a little girl making a very important point. I researched her dress and shoes as well as those of Ella from various historic sources. Phil's suit was researched from a period Sears Catalog.

13) The original photo, circa 1915, of Ella, her brothers, and little sister Doris that Cortney used as a reference for his illustration

14) Phil and John in uniform in 1917

Using the original photo for my direct reference for this drawing, and with information contributed by military history researchers, I was fairly certain that the reference photo was taken before Phil and John embarked for France. Canvas leggings and campaign hats were rarely used once the American Expeditionary Forces landed in France. Wool leg wrappings, overseas caps, and steel helmets were deemed more suitable for combat troops encountering the mud and danger of the trenches.

15) The original photo of Phil and John in uniform in 1917

16) Phil and the neighborhood children

This was another of my favorite illustrations to do. Not based on any photo but relying on much research, my military history advisors helped me to choose even the most inconsequential item in this drawing, that being the clothing bag that Phil has slung over his shoulder—a correct period military item he might use to carry his belongings on a short two-day furlough home before he shipped out to France. Phil wears the uniform issued when he enlisted; campaign hat, pants, and service coat manufactured some years earlier, before the United States had to redesign and manufacture millions of new uniforms for all the enlisting troops. All the research aside, Phil's warm relationship with the neighborhood children was the more important aspect to illustrate.

17) Phil, John, and Warren aboard the *Adriatic*

The RMS *Adriatic* was one of the more difficult ships to research. There are many reference photos of the entire ship, but luckily, two rare high resolution photos of the stern were found which enabled me to draw a scene that showed Phil, John, and Warren, the stern of the ship, plus the Hoboken

U.S. Army Transport Docks in the background. A correct "white ensign" of the Royal Navy flies over their heads. It's possible that for security reasons, the troops were actually kept below until out of sight of land, but in order to show this scene, we're assuming that Phil, John, and Warren might have had special duties to perform on deck at the stern of the RMS *Adriatic*.

18) Phil and John eat in a trench during their time in France

This was another illustration where it was important to research every aspect of the scene. Uniforms, mess kits, weaponry, construction of the trench, and even how the sandbags were constructed were carefully investigated. Sharp-eyed viewers might spot the German gas mask canister near Phil and a broken Mauser rifle outside the trench. This late winter or early spring scene communicates only very little of the terrible conditions for the troops living in the trenches.

19) Phil writing his farewell letter on July 19, 1918

All the elements of the composition of this illustration lead the eye down to Phil sitting in a foxhole writing his farewell letter to his parents. It's July and despite the hot weather, the men are ordered to be totally clothed and covered in their hot wool uniforms with their gas masks at the ready in case the Germans launch a gas attack that could blister and burn their uncovered skin. The case that Phil is using as a support for his letter and which his buddy has slung around his neck, contains the gas mask.

20) Phil as a company runner on July 21, 1918

This is perhaps the most heavily researched illustration in the book. Historical military consultants helped with the details of the uniforms and equipment and French WWI military historian, Gilles Lagin, actually walked the battlefield where Private Edwards fell. It was with Gilles' expert help and research that I was able to reconstruct the tactics and position of Phil's company as well as the landscape and ground on which Phil's final mission took place.

In the illustration, we are standing at the edge of a wooded area known as Breteuil Wood, facing east, about one mile from the town of Trugny which is a little under four miles from Château-Thierry and about 50 miles from Paris. Farm buildings (Trugny Farm) can be seen at the left and the German troops are east and north of Trugny. The Germans are very active with their machine guns and artillery on the open fields, shelling those areas with shrapnel, explosive, and even some gas shells.

Private Philip Edwards of Company H, 102nd Infantry, has a mission as a runner to deliver a message to Company E, in the woods we see in the distance. With radio communications being difficult in 1918, the American Expeditionary Force depends on runners as being crucial for the communication of tactics and strategy.

Private Edwards, with no protective cover, has to run about half a mile in the open to his objective, not knowing if he is facing snipers, artillery shells or machine gun fire. Though he probably carries a .45 pistol, there is no defense against whatever the enemy wanted to throw at him.

The men of his company, taking shelter in foxholes and shell holes, watch their buddy Phil take off at a run towards the distant woods (Trugny Wood). A machine gun position behind the trees scans the distant fields and woods in case they can cover Phil's route and help protect him, but Phil is on his own, out in the open: no defense, no cover, and living the final moments of his life as he carries out his mission.

21) "Welcome Home" parade for the 26th Division in Boston on April 25, 1919

It was on Friday, April 25, 1919, that Boston hosted the "Welcome Home" parade for the 26th "Yankee" Division. A booklet was sold that day to the public that contained the Division's wartime history and the names of the fallen of this division, including Private Philip Edwards.

Using a photo of the actual parade for reference, my pen and ink rendering encompassed the thousands of onlookers and around 100 of the Yankee Division visible from this viewpoint, as they marched down Tremont Street towards Boylston Street.

22) The original photo of the "Welcome Home" parade for the 26th Division that Cortney used as a reference for his illustration

23) Reverend Edward R. Hance reading Phil's farewell letter at his service on July 17, 1921

On Sunday July 17, 1921, at 3 o'clock, three years almost to the day when Private Philip Edwards lost his life during the Battle of Château-Thierry, Reverend Edward R. Hance of the

Naugatuck Congregational Church in Connecticut officiated at Philip's funeral service. To the attending congregation, Reverend Hance read Private Philip Edwards' last letter to his parents written two days before his death on the battlefields of France.

In order to create the illustration of this scene, we are indebted to the Senior Pastor of the Congregational Church of Naugatuck, UCC, the Reverend Gordon Rankin. Reverend Rankin not only contributed his expertise on ascertaining where the funeral service took place, but he also supplied photos of the pulpit area of the church sanctuary. Perhaps most helpful of all, he discovered a rare photograph of Reverend Edward R. Hance that could be used for drawing a likeness of the Reverend reading Philip's last letter.

The illustration shows Reverend Hance reading Phil's letter from the intricately carved pulpit of the church sanctuary. In front of him is Phil's coffin, draped with the American flag and surrounded by flowers given by Phil's loved ones. Hanging in the center, as was custom at the time, is a framed oval photo of Phil in his uniform with his buddy, John Simmons who was a pallbearer at the funeral service. The newspapers called it "... one of the most impressive military funerals ever held in Naugatuck ...."

24) Ella as a nurse in 1921 helping a patient

Ella's sister, Doris, related to the author that, "It was after Phil was killed that Ella decided to become a nurse. She went into nursing at Griffin Hospital in Derby, Conn. She graduated in 1921."

Though we know no details, I wanted to show Ella at work in a typical hospital ward of the 1920s, taking the vital signs of a patient—one of the many duties of a nurse. Hundreds of thousands of wounded veterans returned home to the U.S. after the war, and many of them required ongoing medical care, rehabilitation, and therapy for years after the war had ended. I chose to portray Ella caring for a veteran—perhaps one of Phil's own fellow soldiers from the 102nd Infantry, 26th Division—as can be seen from the items on the patient's table.

25) The original photo of Ella as a nurse in 1921 given to the author by Ella's little sister Doris Wininger Harkins

26) Phil in spirit

In this illustration, I wanted to capture the concept of Phil's spirit returning to Naugatuck. This could be either a literal or a metaphoric spirit. I envisioned Phil in his regular, plain suit, his cap set back on his head, the idyllic summer breeze lifting his necktie into the air … puffy summer clouds and birds in the sky. Phil's spirit strides along a pathway he had taken many times in life. It leads along a rise and down to an open meadow just on the outskirts of Naugatuck where the children he knew still played. The Congregational Church steeple (Phil's memorial service on July 17, 1921, was held at the church) and flagpole that rises above the town's World War I Memorial that bears Phil's name can be seen above the trees that line the meadow. Just in front of the pathway, we can see a small pond, reminiscent of the pond of his own childhood, and we can see some pond lilies, blooming in the summer sun … a pleasant connection to his past and his first meeting with Ella. Phil's image grows more faint as it nears the ground … symbolic of his leaving this physical life.

26th Division leaves for France
Hoboken, NJ - October 27, 1917

CORTNEY
SKINNER

Company runner Pvt. Philip Edwards delivering a message on his final mission — July 21, 1918

CORTNEY
SKINNER

Welcome Home 26th Division
Boston April 25, 1919

CORTNEY
SKINNER

Reverend Hance reads Phil's
farewell letter - July 17, 1921

CORTNEY
SKINNER

Lovingly
Ella

The Story Behind *One April in Boston*

The story behind *One April in Boston* is a fascinating tale in itself. Most of the artifacts shown in this book were discovered only recently. As research for the project progressed, I felt like I was putting together the pieces of a giant puzzle; one that had been disassembled and the pieces scattered many years ago. As my work continued, I sensed that I was doing it for a special reason, but I wasn't quite sure what that reason was.

The desire to learn more about my ancestors began when I was 10. I would spend hours at the kitchen table my father built, paging through the family record section of a Bible that had been passed down in our family for five generations. The Bible was printed in 1812 and once belonged to my direct ancestor Joseph B. Edwards of Boston. An entry listed his birth date as December 29, 1799, and several other entries listed the names and birth dates of his four siblings.

The Bible contained two other notable items. The first was an entry marking the death of a Benjamin Edwards on June 9, 1808, age 43 years, and the second was a yellowed newspaper clipping about Philip Edwards, a relative and soldier who was killed in World War I. I felt that the Benjamin Edwards listed above, born in 1765, was Joseph's father. I was told that Philip Edwards was my grandfather's cousin.

I read that newspaper clipping about Philip each time I opened the Bible. The article, from July of 1921, covered his funeral, "one of the most impressive military funerals ever held in Naugatuck." He had been killed in France in July of 1918, and it took three years to get his body returned to the United States. The article noted that "he lived and died gallantly." It went on to say "The eulogy was made more stirring when a letter, the last written by Pvt. Edwards to his parents on the eve of going over the top in one of the greatest battles in the world's history, was read." It demonstrated that "the dead soldier was brave to the core."

I would read Philip's last letter over and over again. I wanted to learn more about him. I wanted to learn more about the people in those old Bible entries, too. That's where this project all began ... a 10-year-old boy sitting at the kitchen table, telling himself, "someday I'm going to find out more about these people, someday I'm going to tell their story." I didn't have a lot to work with, but I did have that mission.

My father's Aunt Elizabeth had done some research into the family history well before I was born. She claimed there was a relation to a Captain Benjamin Edwards of Boston and a connection to the Revere family. Aunt Elizabeth discovered the marker of Captain Edwards at Copp's Hill Burying Ground around 1925.

I entered the scene in October of 1961. Three years later, my family took me to Boston to visit the marker of my namesake and snapped a black and white photo of the event. I remember that day, the sun shining in my face, my father holding my hand next to a strange looking rock, and that overwhelming feeling of "what am I doing here?" As my interest in the family history grew, I had that black and white photo, the family Bible, and the stories that my father's Aunt Elizabeth had told me as a child. After she died, all of her written research was lost.

My big break came in 1994 at an Edwards family reunion. Ruth Edwards, a relative who shared my interest in genealogy, gave me a copy of an old newsletter called *The Edwards Journal*. The issue included extensive information from Jeannie Edwards Cook, a woman in Cody, Wyoming, who claimed to have a Bible from 1708 belonging to her ancestor, Captain Benjamin Edwards of Boston! The article listed all the family entries from the Bible and gave other information. That information included a reference to the Captain's granddaughter, Sally Edwards, and noted that she had married Paul Revere Jr. It also listed her siblings, including a brother named Benjamin.

I sent Jeannie a letter, and we began to correspond. Research she possessed noted the baptism date of Sally's brother, Benjamin, as April 14, 1765. Other entries in our family Bibles served to confirm the relationship. I learned that this Benjamin Edwards was my direct ancestor. As an adult, he worked as a cooper in Boston. Ben and his sister Sally were the children of Captain Edwards' son, Dolling. Jeannie was related to the Captain's firstborn son, Benjamin 2nd. This is where the story really started to get interesting.

Jeannie began telling me stories passed down in her family about the Sons of Liberty and how family members were involved in this organization. Research conducted later at the Massachusetts Historical Society confirmed that one of Captain Edwards' sons, Alexander, was indeed a member. She spoke about the family tomb at Copp's Hill and stories of how it had been scarred by British musket balls. I told her that I was familiar with the Edwards marker over Tomb Number 5, and she was quite surprised when I was able to describe its exact location. I promised to send her a copy of the photo of my father and me next to the marker.

As our conversation continued, Jeannie told me that a painting of Captain Edwards existed. I was stunned. She responded, "Not only is there a painting of him, but also a painting of his father." As if that wasn't enough, she mentioned that I could also view his father's original desk that the family had brought to Boston in the early 1700s. "Where could I see these?" I asked. She gave me the name of a relative in Plymouth, Massachusetts, and I contacted her.

In 1994 and 1995, I had the paintings and desk photographed. I also hired a genealogy researcher, Joan S. Leland, who was connected with the New England Historic Genealogical Society in Boston. Through Joan's research, I learned that important birth information contained in my family's 1812 Bible was apparently missing from both the Suffolk County records and the National Archives in Washington, D.C. The Bible was indeed the "missing link" in the puzzle. As the research piled up, it began to fill many boxes in my basement. I wondered how I might share it with others. The desire to share my family's story combined with the internet connections in my business soon spawned a unique idea.

In 1997, I offered to create a website for the Paul Revere House. I would donate the site and my expertise in exchange for a Dedication link off the homepage where I could share my research on the Edwards/Revere connection with others. The Paul Revere House accepted. The site, paulreverehouse. org, has been a great success. In May of 1999, I was honored when the Paul Revere Memorial Association elected me to its

Board of Directors. During this time, the *One April in Boston* book project was born. After reading the *Revere Memorial* and learning of the family's Civil War legacy, I decided to integrate it into my story.

As research for the book continued, I learned more about Philip Edwards. I was told that all the children in his neighborhood loved and admired him. Like a "Pied Piper of Naugatuck," he was followed by children wherever he went. My 93-year-old grandmother, Mildred Edwards, was one of those children, and she remembered Phil. She rode in his wagon as he delivered groceries for the local market.

In 1997, an early photo of Phil and his parents was discovered in an attic by a relative. Previous to that, no photos of him had existed. In early 2000, with the help of a friend (Linda Skarnulis) who scanned through numerous rolls of microfilm at the *Naugatuck Daily News*, I was able to discover the content of two other letters Phil had written from France in 1918. From the newspaper articles, I also learned the names of Phil's sweetheart, Miss Ella Wininger, and his best friend, John Simmons.

As I learned more about the 26th Division, I discovered its strong connection to Boston. The Division was formed in Boston in the summer of 1917. In April of 1919, the 26th returned there to a glorious "Welcome Home" parade. Because Phil was killed in France, he never had a chance to return to Boston with the 26th. Through this book, he can finally return to the place his ancestors called home.

Throughout 2000, I sought additional information on the Colonial Edwards family. With the assistance of Michael J. Leclerc, a project manager and reference librarian for the New England Historic Genealogical Society, I was able to discover the exact location of the Edwards home in Boston. By platting tracts of land near the Edwards property, Michael helped me determine that the family home stood on Back Street (now Salem Street) near the intersection with Cooper Street. It was two blocks from the home of Robert Newman and three blocks from Christ Church. After the deaths of Alexander and Sarah Edwards, the property was passed on to the children of Jedediah Lincoln and Betsey Edwards Lincoln.

In March 2000, with the assistance of Helen Wilmot of the Naugatuck Historical Society, I met a wonderful woman named Fran Jenkins. Fran, age 70, is the daughter of John Simmons and Ethel Elliott. John Simmons and Philip Edwards served together in the 26th Division. Fran shared her father's World War I diary with me and located a photo of Phil and her dad in uniform. From Fran, I learned the legend of the "star stone" and the content of a very moving letter her father had written to Phil's parents in 1918. Fran also told me that she was Ella Wininger's cousin and that Ella's little sister, Doris, lived in a nearby town.

Fran took me to meet Doris Wininger Harkins, age 90, several days later. Doris was just wonderful to speak with. Her memory took us right back to 1915. She remembered when Phil delivered groceries to their home. She recalled her sister's love of pond lilies and undying love for Phil. For six years, I had searched for the true purpose of this project. I discovered it the day I met with Doris.

Through *One April in Boston*, Philip Edwards and his sweetheart, Ella Wininger, can continue to have a positive impact on the lives of children. Their story of love and the gifts they gave to all who knew them will last forever. In their name, a donation will be made to the Paul Revere House, on an annual basis, to help fund educational programs for children.

The Journey Continues—
Author's Update 2015

In 2000, when I wrote "The Story Behind *One April in Boston*," which appears at the back of the first edition of the book, there wasn't enough room to include many fascinating details about the search for my ancestors. Over the past fifteen years, many remarkable things have occurred as well, so this serves as an update for readers.

The newspaper clipping containing Philip Edwards' farewell letter from France had inspired me since childhood, but I had never taken the time to visit his marker in Naugatuck, Connecticut. Then, during the July 4th weekend in 1998, I decided to see if I could locate Philip Edwards' marker at Grove Cemetery. I obtained directions to the cemetery at a local service station and drove through an iron gated entrance into a burial ground surrounded by forest. I was the only one visiting the grounds on a very hot day and just about to give up my search after a half an hour when I decided to walk to the far end of the rather large cemetery. Here, I threw up my hands and looked to the sky, realizing that I would have to come back and search again for the marker once I had gotten information about its precise location from relatives. At that very moment, I looked down to my right and spotted a small American flag waving in the breeze in front of a large gravestone bearing the name "Edwards" and, above, the words ...

Pvt. Philip Edwards
Co. H 102ND Regt. A.E.F.
Killed in Action July 21, 1918
Aged 23 Years

Here was the marker for Phil and his parents and just as I had elected to give up my search, I had walked directly to it. A few weeks later, on July 21, 1998, the 80th anniversary of Phil's death, I returned with a floral tribute and left a sheet of paper next to his marker. On that paper were the following items: the text of the farewell letter Phil had written to his parents before going into battle; a photo of Phil and his parents in 1905 (when he was 10) taken on the front porch of the family home; and a picture of a soldier in uniform who I felt was Phil. These photos, along with many others, were discovered in an attic by a relative in 1997. The back of the family photograph was clearly marked so I knew it was Phil and his parents, but the photo of the soldier had no identification on it. In 1999, as my research into Philip Edwards continued, I had the good fortune of locating and corresponding with a very knowledgeable military historian named Gilles Lagin of Marigny-en-Orxois, France. Gilles spent a significant amount of time tracing the route of Philip Edwards and the 2nd Battalion, 102nd Infantry Regiment, 26th Division. He supplied me with photographs, maps, a timeline, and regimental history tracking Phil's final days in France. From Gilles I learned that Phil's name appears on a wall inside the 26th "Yankee" Division Memorial Church at the entrance to Belleau. The stone building is the only memorial in France dedicated to the men of the Yankee Division.

In March 2000, while I was writing *One April in Boston*, I met 70-year-old Fran Jenkins, the youngest child of Phil's best friend John Simmons, and 90-year-old Doris Wininger Harkins, the only living sibling of Phil's sweetheart Ella Wininger. This was mentioned in the first edition of the book but I wasn't able to provide additional details about those meetings. Fran lives just across the street from where her father grew up in the Millville section of Naugatuck, Connecticut. She shared her father's World War I diary with me (John and Phil were members of Company H, 102nd Infantry Regiment, 26th Division) along with other family photographs, letters, and memorabilia. From Fran I learned how close John and Phil were. John always wished he had been with Phil on that fateful day and could somehow have prevented his death. In the end, however, he realized that there wasn't much he could have done. As a tribute to his best friend, during his lifetime John kept a large full-length portrait of Phil and himself in uniform in the bedroom of his home. Fran told me that the colorized photograph was in the possession of a relative in Pennsylvania.

Several days after I met Fran Jenkins, we paid a visit to Ella Wininger's little sister Doris Wininger Harkins who lived in a nearby town. I soon learned that the 90-year-old had a remarkable memory. Her recollections took us right back to 1915. Doris recalled how, as a child, she used to hide when Phil visited their home to deliver groceries for the local market. Confirming stories I had heard from my 93-year-old grandmother Mildred

Edwards, Doris remembered that Phil made his deliveries in a horse-drawn wagon and offered rides to the neighborhood children who all loved and admired him. She let me know that Ella's love for Phil was deep and sincere and she carried it in her heart her whole life. In fact, Phil had given Ella a locket before he went off to France. Ella kept his photo inside and always wore it. Ella died in 1992 at the age of 92.

Doris also looked at some photos I had brought—World War I era pictures from that same lot discovered in the attic in 1997. I believed some of them might contain Phil and Ella. One of these photographs was a copy of the one of a soldier in uniform I had left at his marker in 1998. Much to my surprise, Doris told me that neither Phil nor her sister appeared in ANY of the pictures. Yes. I had left the wrong soldier's photo at Phil's marker and was about to print it in my book! Thankfully, I was corrected by someone who had actually known him!

So, what did Phil and Ella look like? Doris didn't think she had any snapshots of them together, but as we concluded our talk, she asked if I would like to see a photo of her sister. I was anxious to see a picture of the girl Phil had left behind when he went off to fight in World War I. Doris stepped out of the room briefly and returned with a beautiful photo taken shortly after Ella had become a nurse in 1921. It was even signed "Lovingly Ella." Doris was so pleased that I had remembered her sister and had planned to include her in my book that she insisted I keep the photo. After this visit, Fran Jenkins contacted relatives in Pennsylvania and requested that they email me a photo of the portrait of Phil and John that her parents had kept in their room. When it arrived, I was finally able to see the face of the soldier whose farewell letter had inspired me as a child. Another picture of Phil and John as young boys was also located, just in time for me to add it to my book.

A week after my visit with Doris, I received a letter from her thanking me for the flowers I sent her after my visit and letting me know there was one more important detail she had not mentioned during our talk. Doris explained that the farewell letter Phil wrote to his parents on July 19, 1918, was not the only one he penned that day. Ella received a farewell letter from Phil, too. Although that letter and its contents have been lost to time, I'll forever wonder what Philip wrote to her on that July day that kept their love alive for all those years. The knowledge that this letter existed had an impact on me as I wrote the ending of the story. The letter Doris sent me also noted, "so far I have not been able to locate any old snaps of Ella, Phil, John, and Ethel. If I do I'll send them to you." I hoped she might be able to keep that promise.

As *One April in Boston* neared completion, Ella Wininger's personal scrapbook was discovered in an attic by a relative. It contained many newspaper clippings of events that affected her life. Some of these clippings were about Philip Edwards. One of these articles was titled "A Real Hero." It read, in part, "We hope every reader of today's news will read the farewell letter written by Philip Edwards of Naugatuck to his parents just before he went over the top in what proved to be his last charge in the fight for democracy. A more truly patriotic letter could not be penned, and it shows that the writer was ready to do his bit to the last."

The article reviewed "the last written words of a clean, noble, heroic, patriotic young American, a boy who was every inch a hero, and one of millions of men ready to give their lives for the cause of democracy if necessary." It concluded by saying, "There have been many acts of heroism performed by our soldiers in France, but of those who performed them, none was a greater hero than Philip Edwards, who wrote just before going over the top, 'I do not fear death in the least. Remember we are fighting for a good cause.'"

Attached to the last page of the scrapbook was a colorful booklet reviewing the history of the American flag. It contained an image of the 13 star flag associated with the American Revolution and *One April in Boston*. The scrapbook also contained many poems about the war and soldiers who had died in France. Ella seems to have had a strong connection to these words as she dealt with the loss of Phil.

When *One April in Boston* was published in mid 2000, I was sure to get two of the first available copies to Fran and Doris. I again visited Grove Cemetery, this time placing a copy of the book at Phil's marker and leaving behind a wood and metal spyglass, similar to the one passed down to him in *One April in Boston*. A short time later I mailed a copy of the book to Fran's brother Bill Simmons who lived in Honolulu, Hawaii, and received a three-page typed letter from him in September. In it he gave some insight into his dad's friendship with Phil, the kind of man his father was, and the bond all men who have faced combat share.

In late 2001, the audio book for *One April in Boston* was produced and early the next year I relocated from Connecticut to Boston. It was the place four generations of my Edwards ancestors had once called home. I became the first family member to live in Boston in nearly 150 years. On a return trip to Connecticut, a year later, I visited Phil's marker once again.

I was surprised to see that the spyglass I had left back in 2000 was still there. The wood had deteriorated and the metal had rusted but it was in the exact same spot. During this visit, I left a copy of the *One April in Boston* audio book at the base of the marker as a lasting tribute to my childhood hero. A light rain started to fall and I took shelter under a group of trees and stood quietly, contemplating all that had taken place on my journey of discovery. What would Phil have thought about all this, I wondered to myself ... or Ella ... or any of the other people in my story who rest here?

In 2004, I started a private guided walking tour business in Boston where I share my knowledge of the historic sites and the story of my Edwards ancestors told in *One April in Boston*. Later that year I received the sad news that Doris Wininger Harkins had passed away at the age of 95 and learned that she was buried beside her family members at Grove Cemetery.

For the next two years I continued my business in Boston working with students on field trips and giving tours to families from across the country. I had all but forgotten about leaving the audio book at Phil's marker in late 2002 or early 2003 when a remarkable email reached me on June 2, 2006. The subject line was "Philip Edwards."

Here is what it said:

Back in 1999, my grandmother passed away at the age of 101. I inherited her photo albums and found a picture of a man and woman with the handwritten caption: "Phil Edwards, died July 1918 in France." This led me to wonder who this young man was that died in France not too long before the end of the Great

War. My grandmother was born and raised in the Millville section of Naugatuck, Connecticut and was a very popular person. Her mother was an immigrant from Switzerland and was the local mid-wife. I started searching through census records via Ancestry.com and found that Benjamin Edwards and his family lived not too far from my grandmother.

From the Connecticut State Library on-line I found that there was a record of Philip Edwards of Naugatuck that was submitted with a picture as part of a post war questionnaire sent to veterans looking for written stories of their experiences. I went to the library located in Hartford and requested the record pulled from storage and was able to view the contents and have copies made and sent to me. I have these scanned and in e-format.

Then last week while in the state library in Hartford on another family fact-finding trip, I looked up Philip Edwards in the Hale collection of headstone inscriptions to see if he was buried in Connecticut. The record only shows a marker for him stating his age and his service info, Co., H, 102nd Regt. in the Grove Cemetery in Naugatuck. This being the same cemetery where my grandmother rests, I decided to seek his marker out.

He is listed on the same marker as his mother and father with a U.S. flag. At the base of the headstone I noticed a CD case and out of curiosity I picked it up, brushed it off and found the "*One April In Boston*" audio book. This was yesterday and I had to see if I could find its origin. Copyright info states a spyglassbooks.

com but it seems that web address no longer exists. It gives a P.O. Box in Prospect, CT, which is the town where I now live. If you'd like to see the two pictures and questionnaire I have, I can email them to you.

Sincerely,

C. Michael Anderson
(Street Address Removed)
Prospect, CT 06712

A day later, Michael emailed me the picture of a man and woman that contained the Philip Edwards' caption. The complete handwritten caption read: "Phil Edwards killed July 1918 in France" and beneath that "Ella Wininger nurse Derby." Ella had indeed become a nurse at Griffin Hospital in Derby, Connecticut—coincidentally the same hospital where I was born. A photo of Phil and Ella was something I had always hoped to find and this one even had the year 1916 penned at the very bottom. I like to think that Doris somehow played a role in getting this snapshot to me, keeping the promise she had made six years earlier. When I first saw the photo of the happy couple it was as if Phil and Ella had been transported through time to express their love for one another and appreciation for the book that honors their memory. The original photo can be viewed in this section and you can listen to an audio recording of this incredible story at **TreasuredPhoto.com**.

Michael Anderson's grandmother Augusta Ericson, age 18, as she looked
when she photographed Philip Edwards and Ella Wininger in 1916.

Augusta Ericson's Kodak
Brownie Model No. 2 A Camera

In September 2011, after a tip from author James Carl Nelson (*The Remains of Company D*), I had a researcher visit the National Archives and obtain a copy of the World War I Burial Case File for Private Philip Edwards, U.S. Army Serial Number 65385. The file contained information about how he was killed and his burial. Fellow soldiers submitted first-hand accounts.

These included the following:

"We were at Château-Thierry, he was in Battalion Headquarters at the time. Edwards was a runner. He was killed instantly while taking a message. Men in the company gave the report of this to me."

Informant: Fred T. Kochler (no rank given)
Company H, 102nd Infantry
West Haven, Connecticut

"We were being shelled heavily by the Germans at Epieds, in the Château-Thierry Sector when Private Edwards was hit by shrapnel in the right chest. He is buried near Epieds with several other men. He was a company runner, about 5 ft. 5 in. tall and weighed about 120 pounds with light hair and complexion. I had known him about fourteen months. His home is in Conn. and he was well liked by all the men."

Informant: Pvt. Francis Gagon
Company H, 102nd Infantry
Killingly, Connecticut

"Private Edwards was killed at Château-Thierry, and buried by hill 204, the grave was marked. They were marching into a new position, and did so successfully. Stoddard saw Edwards after his death. He said Edwards was killed by concussion, that he had a slight hole in the right side of his chest but that the doctors said that it was not enough to kill him. He was "tiny" good natured, freckled, about 21 or 22, a good kid. Stoddard knew him well."

Informant: Pvt. William Stoddard
Company H, 102nd Infantry
West Haven, Connecticut

"Was killed in Trugny Woods, July 21st, 1918, while the company was advancing on the town of Epieds. Shrapnel thru heart. Burial place: 330 paces east of road from Breteuil Farm to Trugny, 50 feet south of trail, leading east thru woods from above road. Coordinates about 186.5 – 262.8 Map Conde-en-Brie, scale 1/20000."

Informant: Cpl. Howard S. Correll
Company H, 102nd Infantry
West Granby, Connecticut

In the spring of 2012, I contacted military historian Gilles Lagin who had performed research for my book over 10 years earlier. Using the new and detailed information found in Philip Edwards' Burial Case File housed at the National Archives, and original battlefield maps, Gilles planned a trip that summer to see if he could find the precise location where Phil's company had fought and where he had died. On July 22, 2012, almost 94 years to the day that Phil was killed in action, Gilles found the fighting position of Phil's company in the forest, some U.S. WWI cartridge cases, and even the shell hole where Phil had initially been buried with three other American soldiers. Gilles took numerous photos around the place and the view of Trugny from that area noting that the wheat had not yet been harvested, so the fields were much like those Phil would have seen in July 1918.

In 2012 and again in 2014 Gilles made trips to the 26th Division Memorial Church, as he had done at my request many years earlier. During these visits he took beautiful photos (with better camera equipment) inside and outside the church including Philip Edwards' name carved on the honor wall with other members of Boston's 26th Division who made the supreme sacrifice for their country. These photos, as well as his earlier pictures, can be viewed on the website for the book: **OneAprilinBoston.com**.

Today, in 2015, I often think of Philip Edwards. As a child, Phil spent a lot of time fishing with his friends. I did the very same thing. A clipping from 1917 in Ella's scrapbook noted that he was a member of the Company H 102nd Regiment football team. I played youth football myself as a child. Phil's U.S. Army serial number was 65385. If you add those numbers up it comes to 27. Coincidentally, as a 10-year-old, my first number in Pop Warner football was 27. It was at that age that I first read the yellowed newspaper clipping about Philip Edwards and was so moved by his farewell letter. The walking tour I offer to school children and families begins on Tremont Street by Boston Common—along the same route Phil would have marched, had he survived the war, with other members of the 26th "Yankee" Division during their "Welcome Home" parade in Boston on April 25, 1919.

Although I don't have a horse-drawn wagon like Phil, I do have my own modern day version of "children from the neighborhood" as a captive audience. Following in his tradition, I serve as the latest generation of storytellers in the Edwards family. My story is one of a small child who became intrigued by his early Boston ancestors and was determined to learn as much about them as he could. I wanted their stories to survive. Little could I have imagined back then how a newspaper clipping about a World War I soldier named Philip Edwards would change my life. I'm currently pitching *One April in Boston: The Gift of the Spyglass* as a feature film or made-for-TV movie and want to thank my friend Dan Kruse for his encouragement in this endeavor. It is indeed a lofty goal, but aren't those the ones most worth pursuing?

It is my hope that Phil's story and the message he passes along through *One April in Boston* will inspire generations of school children to use their imaginations, set goals, take action toward their achievement each day, and NEVER give up on them.

One April in Boston: The Gift of the Spyglass is available for free at both the Amazon Kindle Store and the iTunes Store. This is in keeping with the story and Phil's goal of passing "the gift of the spyglass" on to not only the neighborhood children, but to every child who believes in it.

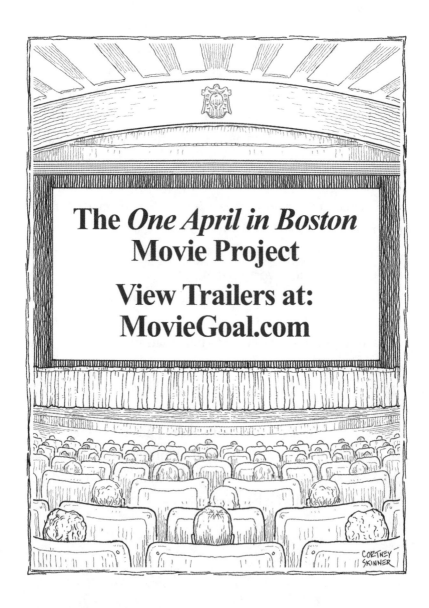

The *One April in Boston* Movie Project

Goal: To turn a children's book that teaches American history, the power of imagination, and the value of goal setting into a feature film or made-for-TV movie.

The movie would be set in the 20th century with Philip Edwards as the main character and flash back to earlier time periods in the book.

Action Step #1: Three videos have been created to introduce the book and Philip Edwards' story to people in the film industry. You can view these videos at the end of this section.

Americans love a great story. Particularly when told through living examples of truth, courage, compassion, and history.

The legacy of Philip Edwards began in his hometown of Naugatuck, Connecticut where he became the idol of his neighborhood's children who loved and admired him for his kindness and attentive conversations.

Phil's glowing example warmed the hearts of all who crossed his path. But, as his heart fell vulnerable to thoughts of spring ... destiny suddenly beckoned Philip Edwards to heed the "patriots" call, like his ancestors before him.

Soon, an average American boy, renowned for his remarkable gift of humility and kindness to children, would summon all courage and make the supreme sacrifice on a battlefield in France in World War I. But this is where the story of Philip Edwards—and his ultimate gift—really BEGINS.

Throughout his childhood, author Ben Edwards was acutely aware of his family's rich American heritage. Beyond the connections to Paul Revere and Colonial Boston, Ben was particularly moved by tales of his relative Philip Edwards, his conversations with the neighborhood children, and the life lessons he passed along to them.

One April in Boston: The Gift of the Spyglass is Ben Edwards' tribute to his family's Boston history. It is also a testament to Private Edwards' special affinity for children ... and centers around one very special gift he arranged to bestow, in the event of his death. Tenderly expressed in the story is an emotional letter written by Philip Edwards to his parents, just two days before his death. In this letter, Phil asks his parents to pass on a message to the neighborhood children.

The book also reveals the timeless love story of Philip Edwards and his sweetheart Ella Wininger. Ben met and interviewed Ella's sister, 90-year-old Doris Wininger Harkins, who shared details of their relationship. From Doris, Ben learned that the farewell letter Phil wrote to his parents wasn't the only one he penned that day. He wrote one to Ella too. Although that letter has been lost to time, Ben wondered what Phil wrote to Ella that kept her feelings of love for him alive until she passed away over 70 years later. The conclusion of the story captures the spirit of that endless love and conveys the powerful impact Phil had on the neighborhood children before his death at the age of 23.

Now included in this newly revised and updated book, is the true tale behind the author's incredible discovery of a photo of Phil and Ella taken in 1916. The events leading to this photo's discovery in 2006 are just another amazing footnote to this remarkable story.

Videos: Three videos were created to introduce the book and Philip Edwards' story to people in the film industry. **You can view these videos at MovieGoal.com.**

The Colonial Edwards Family Tree

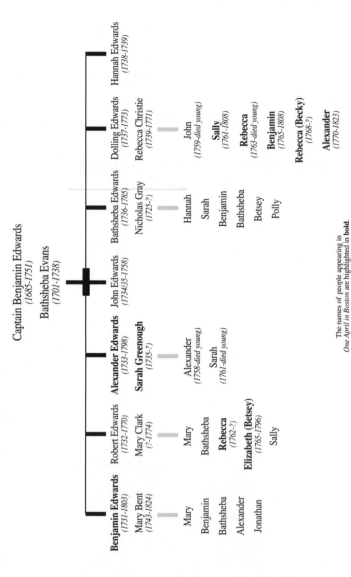

Captain Benjamin Edwards
(1685-1751)
Bathsheba Evans
(1701-1738)

Benjamin Edwards
(1731-1803)
Mary Bent
(1743-1824)

Mary
Benjamin
Bathsheba
Alexander
Jonathan

Robert Edwards
(1732-1770)
Mary Clark
(?-1774)

Mary
Bathsheba
Rebecca
(1762-?)
Elizabeth (Betsey)
(1765-1796)

Sally

Alexander Edwards
(1733-1798)
Sarah Greenough
(1735-?)

Alexander
(1758-died young)
Sarah
(1761-died young)

John Edwards
(1734/35-1758)

Bathsheba Edwards
(1736-1785)
Nicholas Gray
(1725-?)

Hannah
Sarah
Benjamin
Bathsheba
Betsey
Polly

Dolling Edwards
(1737-1773)
Rebecca Christie
(1739-1771)

John
(1759-died young)
Sally
(1761-1808)
Rebecca
(1763-died young)
Benjamin
(1765-1808)
Rebecca (Becky)
(1768-?)
Alexander
(1770-1823)

Hannah Edwards
(1738-1739)

The names of people appearing in
One April in Boston are highlighted in **bold**.

The Colonial Edwards Family

The names of people appearing in *One April in Boston* are highlighted in **bold**.

Captain Benjamin Edwards (1685-1751) married Hannah Harrod (1687-1728) on December 10, 1706, at the Old North Meeting House (Second Church) in Boston. They were married by Cotton Mather. Benjamin and Hannah had three children (Sarah, Hannah, and Benjamin), who all died in their infancy. Hannah died in 1728.

Captain Benjamin Edwards then married Bathsheba Evans (1701-1738) on May 14, 1730, at the New Brick Church. They were married by Reverend William Welstead. Bathsheba was the daughter of Sea Captain Jonathan Evans and Mary Bronsdon.

Benjamin and Bathsheba had seven children:

1. **Benjamin Edwards** (1731-1803) married Mary Bent (1743-1824) in Framingham, Mass. in 1777. (Mary's father Thomas Bent of Sudbury, Mass., was one of the militiamen wounded during the fighting on battle road, April 19, 1775.) Benjamin and Mary had five children: Mary, Benjamin, Bathsheba, Alexander, and Jonathan.

2. Robert Edwards (1732-1770) married first Susanna Downes in 1755 and second Mary (White) Clark (?-1774) in 1756. Robert and Mary had five daughters: Mary, Bathsheba, **Rebecca**, Elizabeth (**Betsey**), and Sally. **Rebecca Edwards** (1762-?) married Caleb Coolidge in 1786. **Betsey Edwards** (1765-1796) married **Jedediah Lincoln**, ancestor of Abraham Lincoln, in 1785. They had six children. When Betsey died in 1796, Jedediah married Mary Revere.

3. **Alexander Edwards** (1733-1798) was a cabinetmaker and member of the Sons of Liberty. He married **Sarah Greenough** (1735-?) in 1757. Alexander and Sarah had a son, Alexander, in 1758 (he died young) and a daughter, Sarah, who died in infancy in 1761.

4. John Edwards (1734/35-1758) was a cooper. He drowned in the river at Philadelphia while returning from a voyage to Jamaica.

5. Bathsheba Edwards (1736-1785) first married a man named Carter. They had two children. Then she married Nicholas Gray in 1754. Bathsheba and Nicholas had six children: Hannah, Sarah, Benjamin, Bathsheba, Betsey, and Polly.

6. Dolling Edwards (1737-1773) married Rebecca Christie (1739-1771) on September 21, 1758, at the New North Church in Boston.

Dolling and Rebecca had six children:

John Edwards (born in 1759) died young.

Sally Edwards (baptized Sarah) (1761-1808) married **Paul Revere Jr.** (1760-1813), son of Boston silversmith **Paul Revere.** They had 12 children.

Rebecca Edwards (born in 1763) died young.

Benjamin Edwards (1765-1808) was baptized April 14, 1765, at the New North Church. He was a cooper in Boston and is the author's direct ancestor. Ben married Mary (Polly) Bangs in 1791. Ben and Polly had five children: Benjamin, Bathsheba, Alexander, Joseph Bragdon, and Maryan. **Joseph Bragdon Edwards** (1799-1852), the son of Benjamin the cooper and direct ancestor of the author, was employed as an innkeeper and a paver in Boston. His son, **Benjamin Edwards**, (1836-1926) was the grandfather of **Philip Edwards** (1895-1918).

Rebecca Edwards (1768-?) married Josiah Carter, a blacksmith. In this story, she is called Becky. Rebecca and Josiah had at least one child, a daughter named Rebecca, born in Lexington in 1790.

Alexander Edwards (1770-1823) a cabinetmaker.

7. Hannah Edwards (1738-1739) died at the age of 16 months.

The North End of Boston in 1775

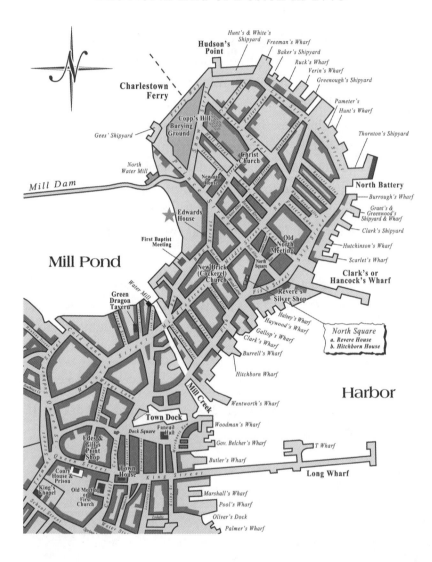

The Edwards Family in Boston

L earn more about author Ben L. Edwards' ancestors who lived in Boston for 150 years as well as how old they were when certain key events occurred in Boston.

Captain Benjamin Edwards (1685-1751)—Born December 15, 1685—Ben's Sixth Great Grandfather

- Age 20 when Benjamin Franklin is born on Milk Street in 1706

- Age 27 when the second Town House (today's Old State House) is dedicated in 1713

- Age 29 when Long Wharf is completed in 1715

- Age 36 when Benjamin Franklin writes his fourteen Silence Dogood letters between April and October of 1722

- Age 37 when Christ Church (Old North Church) is built in 1723

- Age 51 when Thomas Hancock's mansion is built on Beacon Hill in 1737

- Age 54 when the steeple is added to Christ Church (Old North Church) in 1740

- Age 56 when Faneuil Hall is built in 1742 and its grasshopper weather vane installed

Captain Benjamin Edwards was a sea captain and merchant who lived in the North End of Boston. Early records indicate he was on Hull Street in 1713 and at the corner of Prince and Salem streets in 1717. In 1719, Captain Edwards bought property on Back Street (now Salem Street) where he lived for the remainder of his life. Today the address of the Edwards' family property/home site is 104 Salem Street, where L'Osteria Restaurant now stands.

Captain Benjamin Edwards (1685-1751) was born in England. He married Hannah Harrod on December 10, 1706, at the Second Church (a congregational church also known as the Old North Meeting House) in Boston. They were married by Cotton Mather. Between 1709 and 1717 the couple had three children (two girls and one boy), all of whom died in infancy. In November 1719 Captain Edwards and 23 other men founded the New Brick Church. This congregational church was built in 1721 and stood on Middle Street, now Hanover Street in the North End. Captain Edwards would attend the New Brick Church for the next thirty years. Hannah died in 1728, after 22 years of marriage.

Captain Edwards then married Bathsheba Evans on May 14, 1730, at the New Brick Church. They were married by Reverend William Welstead. Between 1731 and 1738 Benjamin and Bathsheba had seven children: five boys and two girls. Among these children were Captain Benjamin Edwards

2nd (born in 1731), a silversmith and soldier in the French and Indian War; Alexander Edwards (born in 1733), a cabinetmaker and member of the Sons of Liberty; and Dolling Edwards (born in 1737), a mastmaker and fifth great grandfather of author Ben L. Edwards.

Dolling Edwards (1737-1773)—Born May 9, 1737—Ben's Fifth Great Grandfather

- Ages 14 and 15 during the town's longest smallpox epidemic in 1752

- Age 18 when the Cape Ann Earthquake strikes Boston at about 4:30 a.m. on November 18, 1755 (Estimated at between 6.0 and 6.3 on the Richter scale—close to 1,600 chimneys in the town are damaged in some way and the Faneuil Hall weather vane falls from the building.)

- Age 19 when the French and Indian War begins in 1756 (his brother Benjamin serves as a captain in the war)

- Age 27 when the Stamp Act is passed by the British Parliament on February 27, 1765

- Age 28 during the first Stamp Act protest when the Sons of Liberty hang an effigy of the stamp distributor, Andrew Oliver, from what would become Liberty Tree on August 14, 1765

- Age 29 when news of the repeal of the Stamp Act reaches Boston on May 16, 1766. Church bells ring and the town soon celebrates with bonfires and fireworks

- Age 30 when the Townshend Acts are passed by the British Parliament on June 29, 1767

- Age 31 when, on September 30, 1768, twelve British warships arrive and anchor in Boston Harbor. At noon the following day two regiments of British troops land at Long Wharf and march up King Street with drums beating, fifes playing, and colors flying to occupy the town

- Age 32 when his brother Alexander Edwards and 300 other members of the Sons of Liberty meet at Robinson's Tavern in Dorchester on August 14, 1769, to partake in a banquet to celebrate the 4th anniversary of their Stamp Act protest at Liberty Tree

- Age 32 when the Boston Massacre occurs on March 5, 1770

Dolling Edwards (1737-1773) married Rebecca Christie on September 21, 1758 at the New North Church. The New North was a congregational church in the North End and the reverend at this time was Andrew Eliot.

Mastmaker Dolling Edwards lived on Ship Street. Between 1759 and 1770 Dolling and Rebecca had five children: three boys and two girls. Among these children were Sally Edwards (born in 1761), who married silversmith Paul Revere Jr., firstborn son of the famous patriot; and Benjamin Edwards (born in 1765), a cooper and fourth great grandfather of author Ben L. Edwards.

Benjamin Edwards (1765-1808)—Baptized April 14, 1765—Ben's Fourth Great Grandfather

- Age 8 when the Boston Tea Party takes place on December 16, 1773 (Ben's uncle Alexander is surely in attendance at Old South Meeting House with many other members of the Sons of Liberty for the meeting held there prior to "the destruction of the tea.")

- Age 9 when the Boston Port Bill, one of the Coercive Acts, closes the port of Boston on June 1, 1774

- Age 10 when Paul Revere makes his Midnight Ride and the Battles of Lexington and Concord are fought on April 18/19, 1775

- Age 10 when the Battle of Bunker Hill is fought on June 17, 1775 (Ben may have watched the battle from a rooftop in Boston as many did that day.)

- Age 11 when the Declaration of Independence is read to the citizens of Boston from the balcony of the Town House (soon called the State House and now known as the Old State House) on July 18, 1776

- Age 16 when Cornwallis surrenders at Yorktown on October 19, 1781

- Age 17 when his older sister Sally Edwards marries Paul Revere Jr., firstborn son of Paul Revere on July 25, 1782

- Age 21 when 20,000 spectators fill the town to celebrate the opening of the Charles River Bridge on June 17, 1786

- Age 24 when President George Washington visits Boston on his tour of the eastern states on October 24, 1789 (Ben may have marched with the coopers as part of the procession of artisans, tradesmen, and manufacturers that was formed to welcome the president.)

- Age 31 when the first Harrison Gray Otis House, designed by Charles Bulfinch, is completed at 141 Cambridge Street in 1796 (still stands today)

- Age 31 when John Adams is elected president on December 7, 1796

- Age 32 when USS *Constitution* is launched from Edmund Hart's shipyard in the North End on October 21, 1797

- Age 33 when the Massachusetts State House, designed by Charles Bulfinch, opens in 1798 (The dome is covered with wooden shingles.)

- Age 37 when copper sheeting, manufactured by Paul Revere at his copper rolling mill, replaces the wooden shingles on the dome of the Massachusetts State House in 1802

- Age 39 when the steeple of Christ Church (Old North Church) is blown down in the "great snow hurricane" of October 9/10, 1804

- Age 41 when the African Meeting House is dedicated on December 6, 1806 (Ben lives in the West End a short distance away on Belknap Street.)

Benjamin Edwards (1765-1808) married Polly Bangs at the First Church of Boston (congregational) on June 22, 1791. They were married by Reverend John Clarke. This church was located near the State House (today's Old State House). Ben was an orphan by the time he was eight and he and his siblings likely lived with their uncle Alexander Edwards at the family home on Back Street. The Boston City Directory of 1796 lists Benjamin Edwards as a cooper on Prince Street. This directory also lists him as a cooper on Back Street in 1798 and 1800, on Ship Street in 1803, on Buttolf Street in 1805, and on Belknap Street in 1807 with no occupation noted. Ben lived on Cambridge Street in 1808. Benjamin and Polly had five children: three boys and two girls. Among these children were Benjamin Edwards (born in 1793), who followed in his father's footsteps as a cooper; Alexander Edwards (born in 1797), a blacksmith; and Joseph B. Edwards (born in 1799), a paver and third great grandfather of author Ben L. Edwards.

Joseph B. Edwards (1799-1852)—Born December 29, 1799—Ben's Third Great Grandfather

- Age 6 when an enlarged Faneuil Hall (today's building) opens to the public in 1806

- Age 16 when the largest bell ever cast by Paul Revere (2,437 pounds) is installed in the bell tower of King's Chapel in 1816

- Age 22 when the town of Boston is officially incorporated as a city on January 7, 1822

- Age 26 when Atwood's Oyster House (today's Union Oyster House) opens on Union Street in 1826

- Age 31 when the first issue of Boston's abolitionist newspaper *The Liberator* is published on January 1, 1831

- Age 31 when Samuel Francis Smith's hymn "America" (better known as "My Country, 'Tis of Thee") is first sung on the steps of the Park Street Church by Park Street's Childrens' Choir on July 4, 1831

- Age 32 when William Lloyd Garrison and others found the New England Anti-Slavery Society at the African Meeting House on January 6, 1832

- Age 37 when the Boston Public Garden is established in 1837

- Age 48 when a 39-year-old congressman from Illinois named Abraham Lincoln gives a stump speech for Zachary Taylor (the Whig candidate for president) at Tremont Temple on September 22, 1848

- Age 50 when the Fugitive Slave Act is passed on September 18, 1850, and slave catchers begin to roam the city. Abolitionist Lewis Hayden continues hiding slaves in his home—a site on the Underground Railroad

- Age 51 when escaped slave Shadrach Minkens is seized and arrested under the Fugitive Slave Act on February 15, 1851, and hundreds of anti-slavery activists rescue him from the courthouse where he is being held

Joseph B. Edwards (1799-1852) married Sarah Mace at the West Church in Boston (congregational) on October 30, 1823. They were married by Reverend Charles Lowell. Reverend Lowell hated slavery and supported the abolitionist cause. The church was one of the first in the country to integrate, giving open seating to blacks and whites alike, and is said to have served as a site on the Underground Railroad. The West Church still stands today at 131 Cambridge Street in the West End.

Joseph B. is listed as a paver in the Boston City Directory for most of the years from 1826 to 1845 at various locations including West Centre Street, Derne Street, 5 Spring Street,

Fruit Street, 14 Second Street, 35 Brighton Street, 30 North Russell Street, and 67 Lowell Street. In 1852 he was at 151 Cambridge Street. Joseph B. and Sarah had five children: two boys and three girls. Their fourth child was Benjamin Edwards born on February 22, 1836. He is the second great grandfather of author Ben L. Edwards and his last ancestor to live in Boston.

Benjamin Edwards (1836-1926) married Mary Elizabeth Sawtell at the First Baptist Church in Boston on April 23, 1856. They were married by Reverend Rollin H. Neale. This church was located at the corner of Hanover and Union streets. Benjamin lived in Boston for about twenty years before moving away (later residences included Chicago, Illinois; New York City; Hackensack, New Jersey (where he served as Town Clerk in 1866); and East Haddam, Connecticut (where he was a farmer after 1870). Ben passed down stories his father Joseph B. told him about how he would walk by Boston Common and see the cows graze (this ended in 1830). He would have witnessed the sad spectacle in Boston on June 2, 1854, of federal troops returning Anthony Burns to slavery.

Ben's marriage record lists his occupation as a jeweler and the Boston City Directory of 1855 shows him working in that profession at 121 Court Street and boarding at 14 Billerica Street. Benjamin Edwards and Mary Elizabeth Sawtell had 10 children including a son named Joseph B. Edwards who was born in New York City in 1861. Joseph B. Edwards (1861-1937) was a yard foreman for U.S. Rubber Company in Naugatuck, Connecticut—a small town that author Ben L. Edwards' grandfather and father (both named Benjamin Edwards) would grow up in.

Tips for Researching Your Own Family History

1. **Begin with Yourself:** List what you already know about your family, beginning with yourself and working backwards. Name your parents, grandparents, great-grandparents, and so on, together with their birth, marriage, and death dates and places whenever possible. Even if you have to guess at some of the information, this process will enable you to see what you have yet to learn.

2. **Prove It:** Once you have listed all you can about your immediate family, determine how much of this information you can actually prove. Do you have copies of records? A birth record can provide evidence of an exact birth date, place, parents' names, address, ages, occupations, and birthplaces of both parents, as well as additional clues that will enable you to link to other records to further your search.

3. **Interview Relatives:** Speak with relatives, especially those who are old enough to remember the stories that may provide unique clues to the past. It is a good idea

to take notes, or to record responses electronically. All stories are worth preserving—as long as you cite the source of the information and do not incorporate them into your family history without first proving their accuracy.

4. **Look Close to Home:** Search for names, dates, places, and other family clues in home sources. Baby books, family Bibles, certificates, old letters and journals, deeds, diplomas, discharge papers, family photographs, insurance records, naturalization papers, newspaper clippings, school records, and scrapbooks are just a few of the sources you may find to further the research of your past. If you do not have these records in your home, try contacting cousins—even distant cousins may have a wealth of information on your family.

5. **Find Published Family Material:** Works that have been published by others about your family may be very helpful to your research. Libraries and genealogical societies have been collecting published family histories for years.

The above text appears courtesy of Ancestry.com, ©2015 Ancestry.com (A MyFamily.com, Inc. Company). For more information on researching your roots, visit Ancestry.com. The author also recommends The New England Historic Genealogical Society in Boston. To learn more, visit AmericanAncestors.org.

A Tribute to Paul Joseph Revere and Edward H. R. Revere

In 1874, the Revere family published a book called the *Revere Memorial*. It was a tribute to two of Paul Revere's grandsons who were killed in action in the Civil War. Those men, Paul Joseph Revere and Edward H. R. Revere, were the sons of Joseph Warren Revere and his wife Mary Robbins.

Paul Joseph began the war with the rank of major, while his older brother Edward H. R., a doctor, was a first lieutenant and assistant surgeon. Both were members of the 20th Massachusetts Volunteer Infantry. During a battle in October 1861 at Ball's Bluff, both brothers were taken prisoner, along with several other members of their regiment. They were held at Libby Prison in Richmond, Virginia. Paul Joseph was soon sent to another jail. By February of 1862, both men had been exchanged for Confederate prisoners.

Before the brothers rejoined their regiment, they spent some time in Boston with their families. Paul Joseph was now the proud father of his second child, a baby girl named Pauline Revere who was born shortly after his release from a Confederate prison. Paul Joseph and Edward H. R. spent a few short months with their families and then returned for duty on May 1, 1862.

On September 17, 1862, both brothers fought at the Battle of Antietam. Paul Joseph was wounded in the arm, and his brother Edward was killed as he dressed a wounded man's leg on the battlefield near the front of the regiment. Paul Joseph was devastated by the loss of his brother. It took some time for his arm wound to heal. In April 1863 he returned to the battlefield promoted to the rank of colonel.

The 20th Massachusetts soon moved from their camp in Maryland to Pennsylvania. On July 2, 1863, Paul Joseph wrote that they had marched to near Gettysburg and that morning moved to the rear of the town. The Battle of Gettysburg, the turning point of the Civil War, soon began. Paul Joseph was severely wounded on the afternoon of July 2. He died two days later on July 4, moments after hearing the news of the Union victory.

After their deaths, in honor of their distinguished service, Paul Joseph and Edward H. R. were promoted to brigadier general and lieutenant colonel, respectively. They were buried side by side in Mount Auburn Cemetery in Cambridge, Massachusetts. Their names, along with those of fellow Massachusetts soldiers who made the supreme sacrifice for their country, are carved in Harvard's Memorial Hall and in Boston's King's Chapel, where they both worshipped.

The Gettysburg Address

Four score and seven years ago our fathers brought forth on this continent, a new nation, conceived in Liberty, and dedicated to the proposition that all men are created equal.

Now we are engaged in a great civil war, testing whether that nation, or any nation so conceived and so dedicated, can long endure. We are met on a great battle-field of that war. We have come to dedicate a portion of that field, as a final resting place for those who here gave their lives that that nation might live. It is altogether fitting and proper that we should do this.

But, in a larger sense, we can not dedicate—we can not consecrate—we can not hallow—this ground. The brave men, living and dead, who struggled here, have consecrated it, far above our poor power to add or detract. The world will little note, nor long remember what we say here, but it can never forget what they did here. It is for us the living, rather, to be dedicated here to the unfinished work which they who fought here have thus far so nobly advanced. It is rather for us to be here dedicated to the great task remaining before us—that from these honored dead we take increased devotion to that cause for which they gave the last full measure of devotion—that we here highly resolve that these dead shall not have died in vain—that this nation, under God, shall have a new birth of freedom—and that government of the people, by the people, for the people, shall not perish from the earth.

Abraham Lincoln

Lincoln produced five manuscript copies of the Gettysburg Address and gave them to various people. Wording in the versions vary. The above text is from the last version he wrote, which is now on display in the Lincoln Room of the White House.

The photograph of Abraham Lincoln that appears in this book was taken by Alexander Gardner on November 8, 1863, just eleven days before Lincoln delivered the Gettysburg Address. The albumen print was produced from Gardner's original glass plate negative by Abraham Lincoln Book Shop, Inc., Chicago, Illinois. It is from the author's private collection.

The country's foremost Lincoln portrayer, Jim Getty, narrated Lincoln's Gettysburg Address for the *One April in Boston* audio book in 2001. This product is given to all participants in the author's Walking Boston private guided walking tour.

Four score and seven years ago our fathers brought forth on this continent, a new nation, conceived in Liberty, and dedicated to the proposition that all men are created equal.

CORTNEY
SKINNER

Philip Edwards' Correspondence from France

The text of the farewell letter written by Private Philip Edwards that appears in this book was taken from the July 18, 1921, issue of *The Waterbury Republican*. I first read a yellowed newspaper clipping of an article that included this letter as a child. Subsequent research has uncovered an earlier article containing Phil's farewell letter in the August 19, 1918, issue of the *Naugatuck Daily News*. The text of this 1918 printing varies slightly from the 1921 version and is shown below. Two significant differences include the addition of the word "forth" in "bring forth peace" and the P.S. added at the very end.

July 19, 1918

My Dear Mother and Father,

We have started a big Allied drive and our regiment is going over the top in a short while. I am writing a short farewell message, which will be mailed to you if I am killed, and if not, you'll never see it.

I have read my Bible, and said my prayers. I believe all my sins are forgiven, and I do not fear death in the least.

I know that it will be heart-breaking news for you to receive this letter. But remember, we are fighting for a good cause and I think this drive will bring forth peace.

Tell all the boys and girls that I died game, and I honestly hope none of them will ever have to get into war.

God bless and keep you both.

Your loving son to the last,

Phil

P.S. Be sure and get your insurance.

I continue to search for other letters written by Private Philip Edwards and members of Boston's 26th Division. One written by Corporal George Victor Lawson, Company H., 102nd Regiment appeared in a Waterbury, Connecticut newspaper on November 11, 1918. George grew up with Phil in the Millville section of Naugatuck, Connecticut, but was living in Thomaston, Connecticut with his parents when he enlisted in the Connecticut National Guard on May 28, 1917.

In his letter to a friend dated September 25, 1918, George states, "We are still fighting and fighting hard. I have been over the top three times and sure have had some experience. I suppose you have read all about the drives we have been on. We are in a rest camp. They call it rest camp over here, but I do not, as we have to drill every day back of the lines. I suppose it rests in one way, not being under shell fire. I wish you could see me now. I am sitting in a shell hole writing this letter and the shells are bursting all around us. I don't mind them now as I am getting used to them."

George closes his correspondence with, "You know if these letters were not censored I could tell you all about it. I am sending you a picture I had taken in Paris, when I was there for two days. It has been a week since we have seen the sun. I will have to close now as the shells are coming too fast."

Corporal George Victor Lawson was killed in action on October 4, 1918, near Saint Mihiel, France. He rests at Saint Mihiel American Cemetery in Lorraine, France.

Photographs, Paintings, and Artifacts

For online access to photographs, paintings, and artifacts that support the children's book visit **OneAprilinBoston.com**. Here you'll see items that have remained in the Edwards family for more than 250 years as well as 20th century photographs depicting people and places in the second half of the story. You'll view three videos including the Book Trailer, eBook Launch Trailer, and Movie Project Trailer and listen to the audio recording "Audio Book Left at Marker Leads to Treasured Photo."

Walking Tour and Audio Book

Walking Boston Private Guided Walking Tour

Meet author Ben L. Edwards on a private guided walking tour of historic Boston. Ben has been a private tour guide in Boston since 2004. Your group or family will walk the Freedom Trail with Ben and see many of the sites you experienced in *One April in Boston* including the Old South Meeting House, Old State House, Faneuil Hall, Edwards Family Homesite, Paul Revere House, Old North Church, and Copp's Hill Burying Ground.

During the tour, you'll hold and read original colonial-era documents and newspapers from Ben's personal collection. These include documents signed by John Hancock and Boston Tea Party participants Thomas Melvill and Amos Lincoln; and newspapers containing ads for Paul Revere's many businesses. Participants receive the 3 CD set and MP3 download of the *One April in Boston* audio book. The product is 3 1/2 hours long and is narrated by Phil Rosenthal who has garnered wide acclaim and numerous awards for his audio recordings for children. The country's foremost Lincoln portrayer, Jim Getty, narrates the Gettysburg Address.

One April in Boston

To learn more about tour options and pricing, visit
WalkingBoston.com.

For information on field trips for school groups, visit
WalkingBoston.com/school-groups.

For information on field trips for homeschoolers, visit
WalkingBoston.com/homeschoolers.

To hear audio samples from the *One April in Boston* audio book,
visit **WalkingBoston.com/audio**.

About the Author and Illustrator

About the Author—Ben L. Edwards

Ben Edwards' passion for genealogy and American history began at a young age. Following clues passed down in his family through five generations, Ben was able to learn more about his Edwards ancestors and their connection to Boston. Someday, he wanted to tell their story. More importantly, he sought to honor his relative Private Philip Edwards by revealing the gift he gave to the neighborhood children before leaving for France to fight in World War I and passing into legend. *One April in Boston: The Gift of the Spyglass* is the result of that effort.

Ben has been a private tour guide in Boston since 2004. He has taught the American Revolution to thousands of students through school author visits and private guided walking tours of Boston's Freedom Trail. Over the past decade, hundreds of families from across the United States and visitors from around the globe have taken Ben Edwards' Walking Boston private tour.

Ben is the founder of Teach History, a company that develops products and lesson plans for educators that help engage and inspire their students. His Primary Source Audio series, a key component of the Teach History line, brings original press coverage of important moments in American history to life.

Ben Edwards has been a resident of Boston for 15 years. He follows in the footsteps of four generations of his Edwards ancestors who called Boston home for 150 years. Ben has served on the Board of Directors of the Paul Revere Memorial Association since 1999. To learn more about Ben, visit **WalkingBoston.com**.

About the Illustrator—Cortney Skinner

Cortney Skinner's artwork appears in books, magazines, comics, and in films. He has illustrated a wide range of subjects including science fiction, horror, fantasy, classics, history, aviation, and children's books.

Beginning his career in the traditional art techniques of pencil, pen, and paint, he added pixels to his palette at the beginning of the digital age. Working in a variety of media and styles ranging from realistic oils to pen and ink illustration, his artwork also includes sculptures of all manner of people, creatures, and esoteric objects. Cortney's conceptual designs and artwork have appeared in films and his landscapes, still lifes, and portraits are found in private collections.

His work for Ben Edwards' *One April in Boston* project began shortly after they met in 1998 at the Paul Revere House in Boston, where Cortney was cutting authentic 18th century style silhouettes for the public—another pursuit he enjoys. Beginning with cutting some silhouettes for Ben's book, his assignment soon expanded to pen and ink illustrations to support the text, and an oil painting for the book's cover. Now

15 years later, Cortney has done 26 original pen and ink drawings for the newly revised and updated *One April in Boston* to supplement the 20 he produced for the first edition.

Nestled comfortably in the Shenandoah Valley by the Blue Ridge Mountains of Virginia, Cortney shares a creative life and abode with his wife, writer Elizabeth Massie. To learn more about Cortney, visit **CortneySkinner.com**.

Credits, Resources, and Bibliography

Author

Ben L. Edwards

Illustrator

Cortney Skinner

Editors

Trish Charles and Michelle A. Larson

Photography

Ben L. Edwards, Rob Edwards, Mike Giannaccio of Visual Concepts Photography, Nikki Machovsky, Devendra Shrikhande, and Chris Steele

Cover Design

Joe Cekauskas of JC Marketing Communications

eBook

Joe Cekauskas, Walt Thiessen, and Brendan Robinson

eBook Converting and Interior Book Design

Lisa DeSpain of ebookconverting

Resources

The following resources were used in the production of *One April in Boston*:

The family Bible of Sea Captain Benjamin Edwards, printed in London, England, in 1708, in the possession of William Benjamin Edwards Jr.

The family Bible of Joseph Bragdon Edwards, printed in New York City in 1812, in the possession of Benjamin F. Edwards.

Correspondence with and research conducted by Jeannie Edwards Cook.

Correspondence and research of Mary Elizabeth Edwards Stevens and Ruth Smith Edwards.

Seventy hours of research performed by Joan S. Leland, CGRS, in affiliation with The New England Historic Genealogical Society, Boston.

Special Thanks

The Paul Revere Memorial Association; special thanks to Nina Zannieri, Director; Patrick M. Leehey, Research Director; and Gretchen Adams, Education Director.

The Massachusetts Historical Society; special thanks to William M. Fowler Jr., Director.

The author wishes to thank Jeannie Edwards Cook and William Benjamin Edwards Jr.; without their research and knowledge this project would not have been possible.

The author wishes to acknowledge the contribution made by William Benjamin Edwards Sr. (1878-1963). He was a great storyteller whose descriptive tales captivated his grandchildren and brought the family's history to life.

Special Thanks

The author wishes to express his gratitude to the late Marion Phillips and her husband Arthur for the hospitality they extended in his visit to view and photograph the Edwards family paintings and furniture.

The author wishes to express his gratitude to Kathryn Coggeshall, Project Manager of the Historic Burying Ground Initiative, Parks and Recreation Department, City of Boston, for her valued assistance.

The author wishes to express his appreciation to Nick Benson of The John Stevens Shop of Newport, Rhode Island, for creating and installing the hand-carved reproduction of the Edwards marker at Copp's Hill.

The author wishes to acknowledge the generous contributions made by the late Dr. Edith Edwards Roos, which helped fund research for *One April in Boston*. This book represents the gift of the family history that she wished to pass on to her children and grandchildren.

The author wishes to extend a special thank you to his parents, Mr. and Mrs. Benjamin F. Edwards; his grandmother, Mildred Edwards; and his good friends Mark and Lynelle Schmidt (models for Ben and Betsey).

The author wishes to thank the following individuals who provided valuable assistance on this project: Gavin Adamson, Frank Bart, John Colwick, Joe Cekauskas, Trish Charles, Pat Geary, Marc Grenier, Doris Wininger Harkins, Bill Jacques, Fran Jenkins, Gilles Lagin, Matthew Lamoureux, Carol Lawton, Michael J. Leclerc, Joan S. Leland, Dan Lynch, Melissa Martin, Ethel Montagno, Carol Moschella, Eileen Owens Pflegl, John P. Salvatore, Linda F. Skarnulis, Don Troiani, Daniel Weinberg, Charles C. Wells, and Helen Wilmot.

Bibliography

A Memorial of Paul Joseph Revere and Edward H. R. Revere. Boston: WM. Parsons Lunt, 1874; Clinton, Mass.: The W.J. Coulter Press, 1913.

"Body of Local Man Killed in Action is Home—Private Philip Edwards to be Laid to Rest Tomorrow with Full Military Honors." *Naugatuck Daily News,* Naugatuck, Conn., July 16, 1921.

Bjerkoe, Ethel Hall. *The Cabinetmakers of America.* Pennsylvania: Schiffer Limited, MCMLXXVII.

Drake, Samuel Adams. *Old Landmarks and Historic Personages of Boston.* Boston: Roberts Brothers, 1881.

Fischer, David Hackett. *Paul Revere's Ride.* New York: Oxford University Press, 1994.

Fleming, Thomas. *Liberty! The American Revolution.* New York: Penguin Putnam, Inc., Viking Penguin, 1997.

Forbes, Esther. *Paul Revere and the World He Lived In.* Boston: Houghton Mifflin Company, 1942, 1969.

"Funeral of Pvt. Philip Edwards Held Yesterday—Eloquent Tribute to Naugatuck War Hero." *Naugatuck Daily News*, Naugatuck, Conn., July 18, 1921.

Gruber, Bill. "A Glorious Rail Station for a Bustling City." *The Sunday Republican Magazine*, August 28, 1988, Waterbury Republican-American Newspapers, Waterbury, Conn.

Havener, James, and Wayne Curtis. *Boston and the Sea.* Boston: The Paul Revere Memorial Association, 1985.

Kay, Jane Holtz. *Lost Boston.* New York: Houghton Mifflin Company, 1980.

Leehey, Patrick. *What Was the Name of Paul Revere's Horse—Twenty Questions About Paul Revere Asked and Answered.* Boston: Paul Revere Memorial Association, 1997.

Lincoln, Waldo. *History of the Lincoln Family, An Account of the Descendants of Samuel Lincoln of Hingham Massachusetts, 1637-1920.* Worcester, Mass.: Commonwealth Press, 1923.

Miers, Earl Schenck. *Lincoln Day by Day—A Chronology 1809-1865.* Dayton, Ohio: Morningside House, Inc., 1991.

Newman Sheets, Robert. *Robert Newman—The Life and Times of the Sexton Who April 18, 1775 Held Two Lanterns Aloft in Christ Church Steeple, Boston.* Denver: Columbia Press, 1975.

Paul Revere—Artisan, Businessman and Patriot: The Man Behind the Myth. Boston: Paul Revere Memorial Association, 1988.

Bibliography

Revere, Paul. *Paul Revere's Three Accounts of His Famous Ride.* Introduction by Edmund Sears Morgan. Boston: Massachusetts Historical Society, 1968.

"Philip Edwards' Farewell Letter Received Sunday." *Naugatuck Daily News*, Naugatuck, Conn.: August 19, 1918.

Robbins, Chandler. *A History of the Second Church of Boston to Which is Added a History of the New Brick Church.* John Wilson and Son, 1852.

"Second Naugatuck Boy is Reported Killed in Action." *Naugatuck Daily News*, Naugatuck, Conn.: August 13, 1918.

Seybolt, Robert. *The Town Officials of Colonial Boston 1634-1775.* Harvard University Press, 1939.

Sibley, Frank P. *With the Yankee Division in France.* Boston: Little, Brown, and Company, 1919.

"Tribute Paid to Philip Edwards." *The Waterbury Republican*, July 18, 1921. Waterbury Republican-American Newspapers, Waterbury, Conn.

Watkins, Sarah. "The Lincolns and the Reveres." *The Revere House Gazette*, Volume 48, Autumn 1997.

Welcome Home YD (The Official Program of the Home-Coming of the 26th Division). Boston: The Everett Press, Inc., 1919.

Zannieri, Nina. "The Revere Family's Civil War Legacy." *The Revere House Gazette*, Volume 42, Spring 1996.

Dedication

This second edition, published in 2017, is dedicated to Private Philip Edwards (1895-1918). One hundred years ago this year, Phil volunteered for service in World War I.

Phil's courage and his remarkable way with children have long been a part of Edwards family lore. I hope his life and this book that honors his memory will inspire generations of children for years to come.

Philip Edwards and one of the neighborhood
children – Naugatuck, Connecticut, 1915

CORTNEY
SKINNER